哈佛蓝星双语名著导读

Today's Most Popular Study Guides

达·芬奇密码

The Da Vinci Code

〔美〕Dan Brown　原著

Sparknotes　导读

谢云中　郝　慧　何晓茵　翻译

郝　慧　何晓茵　校对

张滨江　主审

SMARTER　BETTER　FASTER

天津科技翻译出版公司

著作权合同登记号:图字:02-2007-111

图书在版编目(CIP)数据

达·芬奇密码:英汉对照/(美)丹·布朗(Brown,D.)原著;谢云中,郝慧,何晓茵译.—天津:天津科技翻译出版公司,2009.1

(哈佛蓝星双语名著导读)

书名原文:The Da Vinci Code

ISBN 978-7-5433-2360-5

Ⅰ.达… Ⅱ.①布… ②谢… ③郝… ④何… Ⅲ.①英语—汉语—对照读物 ②长篇小说—美国—现代 Ⅳ.H319.4:I

中国版本图书馆CIP数据核字(2008)第125237号

哈佛蓝星双语名著导读:达·芬奇密码

TODAY'S MOST POPULAR STUDY GUIDES

出　　版:天津科技翻译出版公司

出 版 人:蔡　颢

地　　址:天津市南开区白堤路244号

邮政编码:300192

电　　话:022-87894896

传　　真:022-87895650

网　　址:www.tsttpc.com

印　　刷:唐山天意印刷有限责任公司

发　　行:全国新华书店

版本记录:846×1092　32开本　6.625印张　135千字

2009年1月第1版　2009年1月第1次印刷

定价:15.00元

CONTENTS 目录

致读者

亲爱的读者，在这个多元文化的世界里，渴望知识、钟情文学、热爱英语的你是否希望站在巨人的肩膀上摘星呢?

“哈佛蓝星双语名著导读”系列是全美最风行的经典名著导读笔记，由哈佛学生们融会名著阅读和文学学习精华，亲笔撰写而成。蓝星系列精选了来自世界各国的杰出经典著作，以经典性和流行性并重的名著为素材，以明晰的风格和地道的语言，解读名著精华和具有时代性的主题和思想。每一分册都包括名著的创作背景、人物分析、主题解析、篇章讲解、重要引文释义、作品档案，并且附有相关的思考题、推荐论题、小测验以及延伸阅读篇目。

如今“蓝星”漂洋过海，轻轻落在了国内英语学习读者的掌中，读者不需走出国门，即可轻松掌握哈佛课堂上的知识。蓝星系列丰富的内容编排，使我们不仅仅停留于对名著内容的了解，而且对著作的精华和内涵有更全面、深入的掌握，进而对英语语言和文化做更进一步的了解和研究。蓝星精辟、明晰的编写风格让“半天阅读一本名著”成为现实，使我们在有限的闲暇时间内阅读更多的书，同时迅速增强英语水平，提高文学修养，增加谈资。

天津科技翻译出版公司之前推出的“蓝星”系列78册，多为古典及经典题材，在图书市场上收到了很好的反响。本次推出的新品种20册均以现代及当代畅销书为首选，流行性和可读性更强，进一步丰富了该系列的内容。本次出版仍由天津外国语学院张滨江教授和青年教师负责翻译和审校，并严格按照原作的风格，提供原汁原味的英语环境，让读者自由地阅读、想象和发挥。

蓝星闪耀，伴你前行!

CONTEXT

Dan Brown was born on June 22, 1964 in Exeter, New Hampshire. He attended Phillips Exeter Academy and Amherst College. After college, he returned to Phillips Exeter to teach English.

Although a writer of commercial fiction, Brown's interest in the genre arose fairly late in his life. He read his first thriller, Sidney Sheldon's *Doomsday Conspiracy*, after he had graduated from college. This thriller, which Brown stumbled upon by accident, inspired him to work in the same genre. Aside from Sheldon, Brown has said he admires Robert Ludlum, for his ability to plot large-scale, international thrillers; John Steinbeck, for his descriptive skills; and Shakespeare, for his wordplay.

Brown grew up in a household in which religious and academic topics were discussed openly—his mother was a professional sacred musician and his father was a math professor. This background provided Brown with the confidence to explore some of the complicated conflicts that arise between religion and science. One of his early novels, for example, *Angels and Demons* (2000), examines the conflict between science and religion.

Another theme frequently addressed in Brown's work is the secret society. Brown has said that secret societies hold a special fascination for him, having grown up in New England, where Ivy League universities, Masonic lodges, and seats of governmental power all have their secret rituals and mysteri-

来龙·去脉

丹·布朗1964年6月22日出生于新罕布什尔州的埃克塞特，曾就读于菲利浦·艾克斯特中学及艾姆赫斯特学院。大学毕业之后，他返回菲利浦·艾克斯特中学教英文。

尽管布朗是个商业小说作家，但他很晚才对此类作品产生兴趣。大学毕业后他读的第一本惊悚小说是西德尼·谢尔顿的《世界末日的阴谋》。这本偶然邂逅的惊险小说促使他也开始写作此类作品。除了谢尔顿，布朗还崇拜罗伯特·勒德拉姆（善于写作组织大规模国际化题材惊险小说）、约翰·斯坦贝克（精于描述）以及威廉·莎士比亚（擅长使用双关语）。

布朗成长在一个可以公开讨论宗教与科学话题的家庭当中。母亲是位职业宗教音乐家，父亲是位数学教授。这一背景使得布朗有信心去探寻某些在宗教与科学之间产生的复杂冲突。他的一些早期作品，诸如《天使与魔鬼》（2000年），就探讨了科学与宗教间的冲突。

布朗作品中另一个经常着力描绘的主题是秘密社团。他曾说秘密社团对他有着特别的吸引力。在他生活的新英格兰地区，常春藤联盟、共济会和政府势力聚集地，都有自己带有神秘色彩的秘密仪式。布朗的

ous elements. Two of Brown's novels, *Digital Fortress*(1996) and *Deception Point*(2001), deal with secret governmental organizations.

Yet it was Brown's novel *The Da Vinci Code*(2003), a book that combines all three of these themes, that catapulted Brown to celebrity. So staggering was its success that it inspired readers to return to Brown's earlier novels, belatedly putting them on the *New York Times* bestseller list.

The idea for *The Da Vinci Code*, a thriller that hinges on a trail of clues hidden in the works of Leonardo Da Vinci, first came to Brown while he was studying art history in Spain and learned about hidden symbols in Da Vinci's paintings. While he was researching *Angels and Demons*, his first book, which also has Robert Langdon as the main character and which deals with another secret society, the Illuminati, Brown was confronted with Da Vinci once again. He arranged to go to the Louvre, where he saw many of Da Vinci's paintings and interviewed an art historian. Before writing *The Da Vinci Code*, Brown spent a year researching Da Vinci and reading widely about cryptography and symbology. He also studied up on, and interviewed members of, Opus Dei, a controversial organization within the Catholic Church.

Brown considers himself a Christian and has said that the issues that preoccupy the characters in *The Da Vinci Code* matter to him on a personal level. He has repeatedly insisted that *The Da Vinci Code* was meant to spark further discussion about the mission and place of the Church, not to inspire denunciation of the Church. Furthermore, Brown does not claim that everything the characters discuss is the absolute true. Nonetheless, his novel has been met with a spate of books

两部小说——《数字城堡》(1996 年)和《终极骗术》(2001 年),就是讲秘密政府组织的。

《达·芬奇密码》(2003 年)是一部融合以上各个主题的小说,让布朗一夜成名。它惊人的成功使读者回过头去阅读布朗的一些早期作品,迟来的关注使这些作品随后也登上了《纽约时报》畅销书排行榜。

布朗早在西班牙学习艺术史时就有了写《达·芬奇密码》的想法。这是一本围绕达·芬奇作品中一系列隐藏线索的惊悚小说。在写第一本书即《天使与魔鬼》(书中主角也是罗伯特·兰登,与之打交道的是另一个秘密组织——光照派)时,布朗再次与达·芬奇相遇。他安排了卢浮宫之旅,见到了达·芬奇的众多画作并访问了一位艺术史学家。在写《达·芬奇密码》之前,布朗用一年的时间来研究达·芬奇,并广泛阅读密码学和象征学著作。他还深入研究了天主事工会——一个与天主教会对立的组织,并且采访了这一组织的成员。

布朗自称是基督教徒,他说《达·芬奇密码》中迷倒书中人物的问题对他而言只是个人喜好。他反复坚持一点,即《达·芬奇密码》意在引起人们对教会使命与地位的深刻讨论,而不是去谴责教会。而且,他并未承认书中人物所讨论的问题句句属实。不过,他的小说还是激怒了基督教徒和天主教徒,他们大量著书指责布朗的种种观点,从圣杯、玛丽亚·抹大拉与耶稣的

written by outraged Christians and Catholics, taking Brown to task for his conception of everything from the Holy Grail to Mary Magdalene's relationship to Jesus to the validity of the noncanonical Gospels. Brown has welcomed these debates, insisting that apathy is the enemy of true faith and discussion is the lifeblood of any religion. Brown has also received many letters of support from people inside the Church who appreciate his work. He says that these supporters include nuns who have thanked him for pointing out how ironic and painful it is that even women who give up their lives to serve the Church are not considered fit to serve behind the altar.

After the enormous success of his novels, Brown gave up teaching and now focuses on his writing full time. His next novels will feature Robert Langdon, the protagonist of *Angels and Demons* and *The Da Vinci Code*.

关系，直到未被收入《圣经》的福音书的正确性。布朗欢迎这些争论，他坚称漠不关心始终是信仰的敌人，讨论才是任何宗教的命脉所在。他也收到了很多欣赏他作品的教会人士的来信，他们对他表示了支持。布朗说这些支持者包括修女，她们感谢布朗指出了既具讽刺而又令人痛苦的一点，那就是人们认为妇女即便毕生奉献于教会也不适合在祭坛后履行圣职。

小说取得巨大成功后，布朗放弃了教学，现在全职从事写作。《天使与魔鬼》和《达·芬奇密码》中的主人公罗伯特·兰登将会在他接下来的小说中继续担任主角。

PLOT OVERVIEW

In the Louvre, a monk of Opus Dei named Silas apprehends Jacques Saunière, the museum's curator, and demands to know where the Holy Grail is. After Saunière tells him, Silas shoots him and leaves him to die. However, Saunière has lied to Silas about the Grail's location. Realizing that he has only a few minutes to live and that he must pass on his important secret, Saunière paints a pentacle on his stomach with his own blood, draws a circle with his blood, and drags himself into the center of the circle, recreating the position of Da Vinci's *Vitruvian Man*. He also leaves a code, a line of numbers, and two lines of text on the ground in invisible ink.

A police detective, Jerome Collet, calls Robert Langdon, the story's protagonist and a professor of symbology, and asks him to come to the Louvre to try to interpret the scene. Langdon does not yet realize that he himself is suspected of the murder.

After murdering Saunière, Silas calls the "Teacher" and tells him that, according to Saunière, the keystone is in the Church of Saint-Suplice in Paris. The Teacher sends Silas there. Silas follows Saunière's clues to the keystone's location and discovers that he has been tricked. In a fit of rage, he kills Sister Sandrine Bieil, the church's keeper and a sentry for the Priory of Sion. At the Louvre, Langdon meets Jerome Collet and Bezu Fache, the police captain, and realizes that the two policemen suspect him of the murder.

情节·览

卢浮宫内，一个叫塞拉斯的天主事工会修士抓住了馆长雅克·索尼埃，想叫他说出圣杯藏匿地点。索尼埃告诉他之后，塞拉斯朝他开了枪，并把他扔在那里等死。但索尼埃对圣杯的位置撒了谎。他意识到自己活不了多久了，必须把这个重要秘密传下去，于是他用自己的血在腹部画了个五角星，又用血画了一个圆圈，并让身体位于圆圈中央，以此复制出达·芬奇的画作《维特鲁威人》。他还用显隐墨水在地板上留下了由一列数字和两行文字组成的密码。

杰罗姆·科莱警探给本书主角——象征学教授罗伯特·兰登打电话，要他去卢浮宫尝试解开密码。兰登并没意识到自己已经成了谋杀嫌疑犯。

杀了索尼埃后，塞拉斯给导师打电话，告诉他索尼埃说楔石存放在巴黎圣叙尔皮斯教堂。导师派塞拉斯来到教堂，他按照索尼埃提供的线索寻找到楔石的位置，结果发现自己被耍弄了。狂怒之下，他杀了教堂看守人兼郇山隐修会警卫的修女桑德琳·比埃尔。卢浮宫内，兰登见到杰罗姆·科莱和警察局长贝祖·法希，得知两位警察怀疑自己谋杀了索尼埃。

Sophie Neveu, an agent of the department of cryptology and Saunière's granddaughter, arrives at the crime scene and tells Langdon that he must call the embassy. When Langdon calls the number Sophie gave him, he reaches her answering service. The message warns Langdon that he is in danger and should meet Sophie in the bathroom at the Louvre.

In the bathroom, Sophie shows Langdon that Fache is noting his movements with a tracking device. She throws the device out the window onto a passing truck, tricking the police into thinking that Langdon has escaped from the Louvre.

Sophie also tells Langdon that the last line in the secret message, "P.S. Find Robert Langdon," was her grandfather's way of alerting her: P.S. are the initials of her grandfather's nickname for her, Princesse Sophie. Langdon thinks that P.S. might stand for Priory of Sion, an ancient brotherhood devoted to the preservation of the pagan goddess worship tradition, and to the maintenance of the secret that Saunière died protecting.

Langdon decodes the second and third lines in Saunière's message: "Leonardo Da Vinci! The Mona Lisa!" Sophie returns to the paintings to look for another clue. The police have returned to the Louvre as well, and they arrest Langdon. Sophie finds a key behind the *Madonna of the Rocks*. By using the painting as a hostage, she manages to disarm the police officer and get herself and Langdon out of the building.

As Sophie and Langdon drive toward the Swiss bank identified on the back of the key, Langdon explains the history of the Priory of Sion and their armed force, the Knights Templar. He reveals that the Priory protects secret documents known as the Sangreal, or the Holy Grail. Langdon's latest manuscript is about this very subject.

索尼埃的孙女索菲·奈芙是密码破译部的一名特工,她来到犯罪现场,并告诉兰登必须给美国大使馆打电话。当兰登拨通索菲给的号码后,他听到的却是她的电话留言,警告他处境危险,让他去洗手间和她会面。

在洗手间里,索菲向兰登证明法希正通过跟踪器注视着他的一举一动。她把跟踪器扔到窗外一辆路过的卡车上,警方因此误以为兰登已逃出了卢浮宫。

索菲还告诉兰登秘密留言的最后一行是"附言:找到罗伯特·兰登"。P.S.是祖父对索菲昵称的首字母,意思是索菲公主,祖父以此向她发出了警报。兰登认为P.S.可能代表一个古代兄弟会——郇山隐修会,这个组织致力于维护异教的女神崇拜传统以及索尼埃以死捍卫的一个秘密。

兰登将索尼埃留言的第一行和第二行解读为"列奥纳多·达·芬奇!蒙娜丽莎!"。索菲返回画廊去找另一条线索。警方也回到卢浮宫,逮住了兰登。索菲在《岩间圣母》后面找到了一把钥匙,她用这幅画要挟警官放下武器,并和兰登成功逃出了卢浮宫。

索菲与兰登按钥匙背面的指示驱车前往瑞士银行,兰登向索菲解释了郇山隐修会及其武装部队圣殿骑士团的历史。他揭示了郇山隐修会所保护的是名为圣杯(——译者注:the Sangreal 为古语词,现代的名称是 the Holy Grail)的秘密文件。兰登最新一部著作手稿论述的正是这一话题。

When Sophie and Langdon enter the bank, an unnamed security guard realizes that they are fugitives and calls the police, but André Vernet, the bank's manager and a friend of Saunière's, recognizes Sophie and helps her and Langdon escape. Sophie and Langdon figure out that the number left near Saunière's body must be the account number that will open the vault. When they open the vault they find a cryptex, a message delivery device designed by Da Vinci and crafted by Saunière. The cryptex can only be opened with a password.

Vernet successfully smuggles Sophie and Langdon past Collet in the back of a locked armored car. Vernet turns on them, but they manage to get away with the cryptex, which Langdon realizes is actually the Priory keystone—that is, the key to all of the secrets the Priory holds about the location of the Holy Grail.

Langdon and Sophie go to the house of Sir Leigh Teabing, a historian, to ask for his help opening the box. Teabing tells them the legend of the Grail, starting with the historical evidence that the Bible didn't come straight from God but was compiled by Emperor Constantine. He also cites evidence that Jesus' divinity was decided by a vote at Nicaea, and that Jesus was married to Mary Magdalene, who was of royal blood, and had children by her. Teabing shows them the hidden symbols in *The Last Supper* and the painted representation of the Magdalene. He tells them that the Holy Grail is actually Mary Magdalene's body and the documents that prove Mary's blood line is related to Jesus. He says he thinks Saunière and the others may have been killed because the Church suspected that the Priory was about to unveil this secret.

索菲与兰登走进银行,一个不知名的警卫认出他们是被通缉的逃犯,便给警方打了电话。但索菲祖父索尼埃的朋友银行经理安德烈·韦尔内认出了索菲,并且帮助他们逃出了银行。索菲和兰登猜出索尼埃尸体旁留下的数字必是开启金库的账号。打开金库之后,他们发现里面有一个密码盒。这是一种由达·芬奇设计、索尼埃手工制作的信息传递装置,只有拨对密码才能成功开启。

韦尔内将索菲两人锁在装甲车后车厢里,成功地把他们从科莱身边送出银行。后来,韦尔内却突然翻脸袭击了他们。索菲和兰登最终带着密码盒成功逃走,兰登认识到密码盒事实上就是郇山隐修会的楔石,是解开隐修会保守的圣杯埋藏地点这一切秘密的钥匙。

索菲与兰登前往历史学家雷·提彬爵士的住处,请他帮助打开密码盒。提彬向他们讲述了圣杯的传奇故事。史料表明《圣经》并非为上帝直接所授,而是由康士坦丁大帝收集整理的。他还举例说明耶稣的神性是在尼西亚联合会上经投票通过的;耶稣还曾与有王室血统的玛丽亚·抹大拉结婚,并且有了孩子。提彬给他们指出《最后的晚餐》一画中暗藏的象征性符号,以及其中玛丽亚·抹大拉的画像。他说圣杯实际上指的是玛丽亚·抹大拉的身体,还有一些文件可以证明玛丽亚同耶稣存在血缘关系。在提彬看来,索尼埃与其他人之所以被害,可能是因为教廷怀疑隐修会将公开这一秘密。

As Langdon is showing off the cryptex, Silas appears and hits him over the head. Silas holds Sophie and Teabing at gunpoint and demands the keystone, but Teabing attacks Silas, hitting him on the thigh where his punishment belt is located, and Sophie finishes him off by kicking him in the face. They tie Silas up.

Collet arrives at the castle, but Sophie, Langdon, the bound Silas, Teabing, and his servant, Rémy, escape and board Teabing's private plane to England. Sophie realizes that the writing on the cryptex is decipherable if viewed in a mirror. They come to understand the poem, which refers to "a headstone praised by Templars" and the "Atbash cipher," which will help them arrive at the password. Langdon remembers that the Knights Templar supposedly worshipped the god Baphomet, who is sometimes represented by a large stone head. The word, unscrambled by the Atbash Cipher, is Sofia. When they open the cryptex, however, they find only another cryptex, this one with a clue about a tomb where a knight was buried by a pope. They must find the orb that should have been on the knight's tomb.

Fache realizes that Teabing and the rest of them are in the jet. He calls the British police and asks them to surround the airfield, but Teabing tricks the police into believing that there is nobody inside the plane but himself. Then he goes with Sophie, Langdon, Rémy, and Silas to the Temple Church in London, the burial site of knights that the Pope had killed.

Rémy frees Silas and reveals that he, too, follows the Teacher. Silas goes to the church to get the keystone, but when he tries to force Langdon to give it up, Langdon threatens to break it. Rémy intervenes, taking Teabing hostage and thus

正当兰登展示密码盒时，塞拉斯出现了。他猛击兰登头部，将他打倒。他抓住索菲和提彬，用枪威胁他们交出楔石。然而提彬袭击了塞拉斯，狠狠打在他大腿上系苦修带的地方，索菲一脚踢在他脸上，完成了最后一击。随后大家把塞拉斯绑了起来。

科莱来到城堡，索菲、兰登、被绑住的塞拉斯、提彬以及他的仆人雷米登上了提彬的私人飞机逃往英国。索菲想到只要通过镜子观看，密码盒上的文字就可破解。大家由此读懂了这首密码诗，诗中谈到了“由圣殿骑士赞美的基石”，以及“埃特巴什码”会帮助他们解开密码。兰登想起了一件事，据说圣殿骑士们崇拜鲍芙默神，一个有时被塑成巨大羊头石像的神灵。运用埃特巴什码破译出的密码是“Sofia”(与索菲名字同音)。打开密码盒之后，他们发现里边又有一个密码盒，上面提供的线索谈到了一位由教皇为其主持葬礼的骑士的坟墓。他们寻找的圆球应该就在这位骑士的墓里。

法希意识到提彬和其他人都在飞机上，于是就电话通知了英国警方，要求他们包围机场。但提彬巧设计谋，使警方误以为飞机上除了他以外别无他人。之后，他同索菲、兰登、雷米以及塞拉斯前往伦敦圣殿教堂，那里埋葬着被教皇杀害的骑士们。

雷米放了塞拉斯，并向他透露自己也是导师的追随者。塞拉斯去教堂拿楔石，当他让兰登交出楔石时，兰登威胁要砸了它。这时雷米突然出现并将提彬扣作

forcing Langdon to give up the cryptex.

Meanwhile, Collet and his men look through Teabing's house and become suspicious when they find that he has been monitoring Saunière. Over the phone, the Teacher instructs Silas to let Rémy deliver the cryptex. The Teacher meets Rémy in the park and kills him. The Teacher calls the police and turns Silas in to the authorities. As Silas tries to escape, he is shot, and he accidentally shoots his idol, Bishop Aringarosa.

Silas takes Bishop Aringarosa to the hospital and staggers into a park, where he dies. In the hospital the next day, Aringarosa bitterly reflects that Teabing tricked him into helping with his murderous plan by claiming that if the Bishop delivered the Grail to him, he would help the Opus Dei regain favor with the Church.

Sophie's and Langdon's research leads them to the discovery that Sir Isaac Newton is the knight they are looking for, the one buried by a Pope, because they learn he was buried by Alexander Pope. They go to Westminster Abbey, where Newton is buried. There, the Teacher lures them to the garden with a note saying he has Teabing. They go there only to discover that Teabing himself is the Teacher. Teabing suspected that Saunière had decided not to release the secret of the Priory of Sion, because the Church threatened to kill Sophie if the secret was released. Wanting the secret to be public knowledge, he had decided to find the Grail himself.

Teabing gives Langdon the cryptex and asks Langdon and Sophie to help him open it. Langdon figures out that the password is apple—the orb missing from Newton's tomb. He opens the cryptex and secretly takes out the papyrus. Then he throws the empty cryptex in the air, causing Teabing to drop

人质，以此要挟兰登交出密码盒。

与此同时，科莱和手下人搜查了提彬的住处，发现他一直在监听索尼埃，这让他们心生怀疑。导师在电话中指示塞拉斯让雷米把密码盒给他送来。导师和雷米在公园碰头并杀了他。随后导师拨通了警方的电话，向他们告发了塞拉斯。塞拉斯逃跑时被警方击中，他企图还击，不料却射中了他的偶像阿林加洛沙主教。

塞拉斯将主教送进医院，然后跌跌撞撞地走进公园并死在了那里。第二天，阿林加洛沙在医院里苦痛地回忆着往事。提彬曾经声称如果主教能将圣杯交给他，他就帮助天主事工会重获教廷的恩宠，他以此诱骗阿林加洛沙帮他实施凶残的计划。

索菲和兰登继续进行调查，他们发现伊萨克·牛顿爵士就是他们要找的那个由亚历山大·蒲柏(——译者注：其英文姓名为 A Pope，与“一位教皇”的拼写相似)主持葬礼的骑士。于是两人来到安葬牛顿的威斯敏斯特教堂。在那里，导师用一张留言将他们骗进花园。来到花园后，他们发现提彬就是导师本人。提彬怀疑索尼埃已经决定不公布郇山隐修会的秘密，因为教廷威胁如果他泄露秘密，他们将会杀死索菲。但是提彬想把这秘密公之于众，因而决定自己去寻找圣杯。

提彬把密码盒交给兰登，让兰登和索菲帮他打开。兰登经过一番琢磨，终于明白密码就是苹果——牛顿墓冢失落的圆球。他打开密码盒，悄悄地取出纸莎草卷。然后他把密码盒扔向空中，提彬由于担心里

his pistol as he attempts to catch it and prevent the map inside from being destroyed. Suddenly, Fache bursts into the room and arrests Teabing.

The papyrus inside the second cryptex directs Sophie and Langdon to Scotland, where Sophie finds her brother and her grandmother. During the reunion, she discovers that her family is, indeed, of the bloodline of Jesus and Mary Magdalene. Sophie and Langdon part, promising to meet in Florence in a month. Back in Paris, Langdon comprehends the poem, which leads him to the small pyramid built into the ground in the Louvre, where he is sure the Grail must be hidden.

面的地图被破坏，扔掉了手枪，试图去抓密码盒。这时法希突然冲进来，逮住了提彬。

第二个密码盒里的纸莎草卷指引索菲与兰登来到苏格兰，索菲在那里找到了她的祖母和弟弟。团聚时，索菲了解到自己的家庭的确承袭了耶稣基督与玛丽亚·抹大拉的血脉。索菲与兰登两人分手告别，约定下个月在佛罗伦萨见面。重返巴黎后，兰登领悟了密码诗的含义，并在它的指引下来到位于卢浮宫地下的小金字塔旁，他确信圣杯就藏在这里。

CHARACTER LIST

Manuel Aringarosa

Bishop of Opus Dei. Aringarosa is conservative in his religious views and longs for the Church to return to strict ways. He has affection for material things that represent the power of his order. He is kind to Silas.

Sister Sandrine Bieil

Nun and keeper of the Church of Saint-Suplice. She favors loosening of church strictures and modernizing of the church, and she objects to Opus Dei's attitude toward women. She is murdered by Silas while acting as a sentry for the Priory of Sion.

Marie Chauvel

Sophie's grandmother and Saunière' wife. A kind and smart woman, Mary Chauvel is part of the Priory's plan to keep the secret. She is a descendent of Jesus and Mary Magdalene.

Jerome Collet

An agent with the French Judicial Police. In some ways the classic bumbling police officer, Collet commits numerous errors during the pursuit of Sophie and Langdon. His missteps contrast with Fache's efficiency. He believes in Sophie's innocence, however, and proves himself to Fache in the end.

角色·亮相

曼努埃尔·阿林加洛沙

天主事工会主教。阿林加洛沙宗教观念保守，期待教廷能恢复传统，从严治教。他特别喜爱能体现自身权威的物品，对塞拉斯也很和善。

修女桑德琳·比埃尔

圣叙尔皮斯教堂修女兼看守人。她赞成减少对教会的苛责以及教会要跟上时代发展，反对天主事工会对女性采取的态度。她在向郇山隐修会报警时被塞拉斯杀害。

玛丽·肖维尔

索菲的祖母，索尼埃之妻。一位仁慈、聪敏的女性，她是郇山隐修会保守秘密计划的一部分，也是玛丽亚·抹大拉和耶稣的后裔。

杰罗姆·科莱

法国司法警察。在某些方面上他可被称为典型的笨手笨脚的警官，在追踪索菲与兰登过程中犯了无数错误。他的失策和法希的能干形成了鲜明对比。他相信索菲清白无辜，但直到故事结尾才得以向法希证明这点。

Simon Edwards

The executive services officer of Biggin Hill Airport south of London. Edwards is accustomed to fulfilling the every desire of the very rich, as the airport serves the private business community.

Bezu Fache

The captain of the French Judicial Police. Nicknamed "the Bull," Fache is strong, strong-willed, and religious. He has great faith in the use of technology in his work, which sometimes leads him down the wrong road. Fache's policing methods are a bit unorthodox, but he is good at heart. The name Fache is very similar to faché, which is French for "angry."

Jonas Faukman

Langdon's editor. He is a classic New York publishing type. Faukman is eager to make money, but he is also a cultured and classy man.

Pamela Gettum

The religious librarian at Kings College. A kindly soul, Gettum is willing to help Sophie and Langdon in their search.

Claude Grouard

A security warden at the Louvre. Grouard is a good man who was a friend of Saunière's.

Robert Langdon

The male protagonist of the novel. Langdon, a professor of symbology at Harvard, is honest and trustworthy. He is also

西蒙·爱德华兹

伦敦南部比金山机场的行政官员。由于机场为私人商务服务,所以爱德华兹习惯了满足富有人士的任何要求。

贝祖·法希

法国司法警察局局长。因其身材健壮、意志顽强和无比虔诚,被人昵称为"公牛"。他坚信在工作上应用技术手段,而这有时会让他误入歧途。尽管他的侦破方法有些不合常规,但他心地善良。他的姓氏"法希"与法文中"愤怒"一词发音十分接近。

约纳斯·福克曼

兰登的编辑,一个典型的纽约出版业者。他热衷赚钱,但富有教养,素质较高。

帕梅拉·格塔姆

国王学院宗教图书馆馆员。格塔姆友好亲切,十分乐于帮助兰登和索菲搜索资料。

克罗德·格鲁阿德

卢浮宫博物馆安全警卫。他是个好人,同时也是索尼埃的朋友。

罗伯特·兰登

小说男主人公。哈佛大学符号学教授,为人正直,值得信赖。在学术上极为成功,出版过数本著作。虽然

an extremely successful academic and the author of several books. Although he studies religion, Langdon does not profess any particular religion and prefers to remain an outside observer in matters of faith. He, like Sophie, has a great affection for puzzles of all kinds.

Rémy Legaludec

Manservant to Leigh Teabing and participant in the plot to recover the Grail. Rémy is a mercenary who gets involved in the plot only for the money.

Sophie Neveu

A cryptologist with the French Judicial Police, and the female protagonist of the novel. Sophie, who is about thirty years old, is attractive, single, compassionate, and very intelligent. She was raised by her grandfather after her parents, brother, and grandmother died in a car accident, and her grandfather instilled in her a love of puzzles and codes. In her twenties, Sophie trained in Britain in cryptology. In the novel, she is one of the major players who attempt to crack her grandfather's code. She is also a descendent of Jesus and Mary Magdalene.

Jacques Saunière

The curator at the Louvre, and Sophie's grandfather. His murder sets off the chain of events that takes place in the novel. Saunière's scholarly passions include Leonardo Da Vinci, goddess iconography, and puzzles. He is also secretly the head of the Priory of Sion, the secret brotherhood charged with protecting the Grail, and a descendent of Jesus and Mary Magdalene.

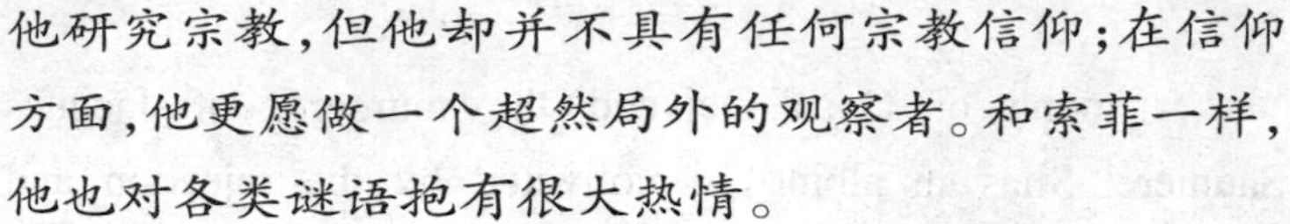

他研究宗教,但他却并不具有任何宗教信仰;在信仰方面,他更愿做一个超然局外的观察者。和索菲一样,他也对各类谜语抱有很大热情。

雷米·雷格鲁德

雷·提彬的男仆,参与了找到圣杯的阴谋。雷米唯利是图,卷入此事完全是为了金钱。

索菲·奈芙

法国司法警察部门密码破译人员, 小说女主人公。索菲大约30岁,外貌迷人,单身,富有同情心,还十分聪颖。父母、弟弟和祖母死于车祸后,由祖父抚养成人,正是祖父培养了她对谜语和密码的热爱。她20多岁时曾在英国接受过密码学培训。在小说中,索菲是试图破译祖父所留密码的重要人物之一,同时她也是耶稣和玛丽亚·抹大拉的一位后裔。

雅克·索尼埃

卢浮宫博物馆馆长,索菲的祖父。他被谋杀引出了全书一系列事件的发生。索尼埃的学术兴趣包括研究列奥纳多·达·芬奇、女神符号学以及谜语。其秘密身份是负责保护圣杯的秘密兄弟会——郇山隐修会的首领,他也是耶稣和玛丽亚·抹大拉的后裔之一。

Silas

A monk of Opus Dei, and the murderer of Jacques Saunière. Silas, an albino, is motivated by the rejection and horror he has faced since he was young. When he falls into the orbit of Bishop Aringarosa, he finds religion and devotes himself to the strict Catholic ways of Opus Dei. He is obsessed with self-punishment and celibacy, and his goal in life is to aid the Bishop and Opus Dei.

Leigh Teabing

An historian and the antagonist of the novel. Sir Leigh Teabing is a knight, a Royal Historian, and an extremely wealthy man. He is crippled from polio and is not married. The Holy Grail has been his one passion for years, and the search for the Truth, which he believes to be present in the Grail, obsesses him. Eventually, his need to know turns him into a murderer. He creates an alter ego, the Teacher, who carries out his evil plot.

André Vernet

The president of the Paris branch of the Depository Bank of Zurich. Vernet was a friend to Jacques Saunière, and sworn protector of his secret. The immaculately groomed Vernet lives among the rich but wishes only to be immersed in culture.

Vittoria

A woman in Langdon's past. She appears only in his memory and demonstrates the difficulty he has maintaining relationships.

塞拉斯

天主事工会修士，谋杀雅克·索尼埃的凶手。塞拉斯患有白化病，由于年轻时缺乏父母关爱，在加上面对种种惨痛，使他做出了许多暴虐之事。在阿林加洛沙主教的庇护下，他建立了宗教信仰，并且严格遵守天主事工会的修行戒律。他醉心于自我惩罚和独身生活，其人生目标是帮助主教和天主事工会。

雷·提彬

历史学家，小说主人公之一。提彬爵士是位骑士和皇家历史学家，并且极为富有。因小儿麻痹症致瘸，未婚。他对圣杯倾注了多年的热情，着迷于搜寻圣杯真相，他相信真相就体现在圣杯本身。最终对真相的渴求将他变成了谋杀犯。他将自己塑造成知己兼导师的角色以实施他邪恶的阴谋。

安德烈·韦尔内

苏黎世储蓄银行巴黎分行行长。作为索尼埃的朋友，他发誓保护秘密。尽管他身处繁华之地，衣着光鲜亮丽，但他只想埋头文化氛围之中。

维多利亚

兰登曾经的女友。她仅在兰登的记忆中出现过，并且表示双方要继续保持关系存在某些困难。

ANALYSIS OF MAJOR CHARACTERS

Robert Langdon

Langdon, the novel's protagonist, anchors the story. He is likable, capable, and goodhearted. Langdon is trustworthy, as is Sophie, his female counterpart and love interest. This trustworthiness makes him stand out in a narrative in which the author casts doubt on the motivations of every major character except Langdon and Sophie. In the novel's many moments of uncertainty, Langdon's presence is consistently reassuring.

Although he is seen as a sex symbol in the academic world, Langdon is clumsy and inept with guns and weapons and lacks resolve when it comes to planning and executing action. He would rather think about codes and symbols than figure out how to escape the Louvre under the eyes of policemen. For this reason, he is balanced well by Sophie, who transforms his intellectual abilities into survival skills that are applicable to real life.

Sophie Neveu

Neveu's presence in the novel embodies the Chinese idea of yin and yang, or two complementary forces that work together in harmony. From Langdon and Teabing, Sophie learns that pagan religions and the Priory valued balance between male and female. Sophie and Langdon form the male and female halves of a single protagonist, and their goals never diverge. In this way, they echo Teabing's and Langdon's ideas about the partnership of Jesus and Mary Magdalene. In their

主角·赏

罗伯特·兰登

兰登是小说主人公，也是全书的核心。他讨人喜欢，能力卓著，心地善良。像他的女性搭档和心中所爱索菲一样，值得人们信赖。当作者对除兰登和索菲以外的每个主要角色的动机提出质疑时，这种可信赖感就会被突显出来。在书中众多悬疑时刻，兰登的出场总能令人安心。

尽管人们将兰登视为学术领域中的男性象征，但他却笨手笨脚，而且不擅长使用枪械。在需要进行谋划和实施行动时，也缺乏解决问题的能力。与在警方眼皮底下想方设法逃出卢浮宫相比，他更愿意思考密码和象征符号。而索菲却能将兰登的知识技能转化为现实中的生存技巧，从而与兰登这个角色达到了很好的平衡。

索菲·奈芙

奈芙的出场体现了中国的阴阳观念，抑或两种和谐互补、共同作用的力量。索菲从兰登和提彬那里了解到，异教信仰和隐修会都很重视男女两性之间的平衡。兰登和索菲各自构成了一个单独的主人公中男女两性部分，而且二人的目标从未有过分歧。他们由此呼应了兰登和提彬关于耶稣和玛丽亚·抹大拉是同道伙伴的观点。在他们看来，男人和女人可为同一目标

view, the male and the female worked together toward a goal, without the female being subordinate to the male in any way.

Both Sophie and Langdon, like the *Mona Lisa*, exhibit male and female traits: for example, Langdon's headiness is balanced by Sophie's real world know-how. Sophie is quick-witted, agile, devious when she needs to be, and physically assertive, as when she helps to disable Silas in the chateau. But at the same time, she is caring and compassionate. She feels the loss of her family deeply and mourns the death of her grandfather. Both brilliant and sexually attractive, Sophie combines a masculine toughness with typically feminine qualities.

Leigh Teabing

Initially, Teabing is a welcome benefactor for Sophie and Langdon. His estate, Château Villette, with its gorgeous sitting room and enormous, book-lined study, seems to be an appealing embodiment of its owner. Teabing supplies much-needed comic relief, and he banters with his manservant and with Sophie as if he were a rich and dotty old uncle. His Land Rover and the bribes he gives to his pilot at the airfield in France help Sophie and Langdon escape from the police.

Soon enough, though, Brown reveals that Teabing is a murderer. After his true identity is known, Teabing turns into a living example of the way wealth can corrupt. Teabing, who has always lived a privileged life, convinces himself that his money entitles him to the knowledge of the Grail's location. His ballroom-turned-study, which at first seems charmingly cluttered, begins to look like the crazy lair of a serial killer. His jokes turn from entertaining to manipulative. And his habit of throwing money around, bribing people in order to ensure

协作,而女人在任何方面均不从属于男人。

索菲和兰登就像《蒙娜丽莎》这幅画,彰显了男女两性的特征。例如,兰登的冲动冒失恰恰与索菲具有的实际知识相平衡。索菲机智敏捷,能随机应变,行动起来坚定自信,我们可以从她在城堡中协助提彬等人制服塞拉斯时看出她的这些特点。但与此同时,她又兼具爱心和同情心。她对失去家人哀痛至深,对祖父被害极度悲痛。索菲头脑敏锐并富有女性魅力,她身上融合了男性的坚韧与女性的特质。

雷·提彬

对索菲和兰登来说,提彬起初是位受人欢迎的恩人。他的庄园维莱特城堡,以及其中辉煌壮丽的起居室,书籍林立的书房,似乎都成了主人的迷人化身。提彬不乏喜剧色彩地满足了两人急需的援助, 又和男仆、索菲打趣,仿佛自己是个富有、古怪的老叔叔。他驾驶陆虎汽车,并在法国机场向飞行员行贿,成功地帮助索菲和兰登逃脱了警方的追捕。

但时间不长, 布朗就揭开了提彬谋杀犯的面目。在被揭穿真实身份之后,提彬便成了富而不仁的鲜活事例。一直过着特权生活的提彬,坚信金钱能让自己得知圣杯藏匿的地方。他那间由舞厅改造的书房,第一眼看去似乎内容充实、令人着迷,现在则更像是连环杀人犯藏身的疯狂巢穴;而他的笑话也从令人开心变成意在操控他人。提彬乱扔钱的习惯,以及为让大家从法国安全脱身向他人行贿的行为,此刻都显得自

the group's safe passage out of France, seems self-serving.

Teabing is willing to go to any lengths to get what he wants, no matter who he hurts along the way. In some sense, his desire to expose the truth about the Grail can be seen as noble. But by the end of the novel, it is clear that he is really out to satisfy his own perverse obsession, not to find truth.

私自利。

为了达到目的，提彬会竭尽全力，而不顾及由此会伤害到谁。从某种意义上看，他揭开圣杯真相的欲望可被视为高尚之举，但在小说结尾，我们发现他的所作所为不过是为了满足自己痴狂的想法，而并非为了探寻真相。

THEMES, MOTIFS & SYMBOLS

Themes

Themes are the fundamental and often universal ideas explored in a literary work.

The False Conflict between Faith and Knowledge

Dan Brown refuses to accept the idea that faith in God is rooted in ignorance of the truth. The ignorance that the Church has sometimes advocated is embodied in the character of Bishop Aringarosa, who does not think the Church should be involved in scientific investigation. According to *The Da Vinci Code*, the Church has also enforced ignorance about the existence of the descendents of Jesus. Although at one point in the novel Langdon says that perhaps the secrets of the Grail should be preserved in order to allow people to keep their faith, he also thinks that people who truly believe in God will be able to accept the idea that the Bible is full of metaphors, not literal transcripts of the truth. People's faith, in other words, can withstand the truth.

The Subjectivity of History

The Da Vinci Code raises the question of whether history books necessarily tell the only truth. The novel is full of reinterpretations of commonly told stories, such as those of Jesus' life, the pentacle, and the Da Vinci fresco *The Last Supper*. Brown provides his own explanation of how the Bible was compiled and of the missing gospels. Langdon even interprets

主题·主题成分·象征

主题

主题是一部文学作品所探索的基本的、常常是带有普遍性的思想。

信仰与知识的错误之争

丹·布朗拒绝接受信仰上帝源于对真理的无知这一观点。阿林加洛沙主教认为教会不应当参与科学调查,这个人物正体现了教会在某些时候对这种无知的支持。按照《达·芬奇密码》的说法,教会对耶稣后裔存在一事也强制推行了愚民政策。尽管兰登在书中某处曾提到,为使人们保持信仰也许应该保守有关圣杯的真相,但他同时认为真心信奉上帝的人们可以接受这一观点,即圣经中充满了隐喻,而不是对事实的照本宣科。换言之,人们的信仰可与真相相抗衡。

历史的主观性

《达·芬奇密码》提出了一个问题:历史书籍是否必须讲述唯一的真相?书中重新解读了众多人们耳熟能详的故事,诸如耶稣的生活、五角星和达·芬奇的湿壁画《最后的晚餐》。布朗对圣经如何被编纂以及失落的圣杯做出了自己的解释。兰登甚至重新解读了迪斯

the Disney movie *The Little Mermaid*, recasting it as an attempt by Disney to show the divine femininity that has been lost. All of these retellings are presented as at least partly true.

The Intelligence of Women

Characters in *The Da Vinci Code* ignore the power of women at their peril. Throughout the novel, Sophie is underestimated. She is able to sneak into the Louvre and give Langdon a secret message, saving him from arrest, because Fache does not believe her to be capable of doing her job. Fache specifically calls Sophie a "female cryptologist" when he is expressing his doubts about Sophie and Langdon's ability to evade Interpol. When interpreting one of the clues hidden in the rose box, Langdon and Teabing leave Sophie out, completely patronizing her. When she is finally allowed to see the clue, she immediately understands how to interpret it. Sophie saves Langdon from arrest countless times.

Other women are similarly underestimated. Sister Sandrine, in the Church of Saint-Suplice, is a sentry for the Brotherhood, but Silas, indoctrinated in the hypermasculine ways of Opus Dei, does not consider her a threat. And Marie Chauvel, Sophie's grandmother, manages to live without incident near Rosslyn Chapel for years, preserving her bloodline through Sophie's brother.

Motifs

Motifs are recurring structures, contrasts, or literary devices that can help to develop and inform the text's major themes.

尼的电影《小美人鱼》,将其视为迪斯尼向人们说明遗失的神圣女性的一次尝试。所有的这些复述至少在一定程度上被看作是真实的。

女性的智慧

《达·芬奇密码》中忽视女性力量的角色都是在拿自己冒险。纵观全书,索菲始终是一个被忽略的角色。因为法希不相信她能胜任工作,于是她潜入卢浮宫并给兰登发送密信,使他免遭逮捕。法希质疑索菲和兰登是否有能力摆脱国际刑警组织追捕时,他特别用“女密码破译员”这个词来称呼她。提彬和兰登解读玫瑰盒中所藏线索时也将索菲撇在一边,全然不顾她的存在。最终一旦他们允许索菲看到线索,她立即就明白了该如何解读它。正是索菲无数次解救了兰登,使他免遭逮捕。

其他女性角色也处于类似的被忽略的地位。圣叙尔皮斯教堂的修女桑德琳·比埃尔是兄弟会的警卫,但被天主事工会灌输绝对大男子主义思想的塞拉斯并没有将她视为威胁。此外,索菲的祖母玛丽·肖维尔在罗斯林教堂附近安然生活多年,将她的血脉通过索菲的弟弟得以保存。

主题成分

主题成分是指有助于逐步展现并形成文本主题的再现结构、对比或文学手段。

Ancient and Foreign Languages

Many of the secrets that lie below the surface of the narrative are concealed from would-be interpreters only by language. Saunière leaves anagrams for Sophie to decipher. Langdon and Teabing use the Hebrew alphabet to figure out a clue. Sophie helps Langdon and Teabing use a mirror to read the backward writing that Da Vinci favored. In *The Da Vinci Code*, language reminds us that secrets exist everywhere and sometimes need just a little interpretation.

Art

Brown uses descriptions of works of fine art to prove that art can tell stories that history tends to obscure. These works of art include Da Vinci's *Last Supper*, *Madonna of the Rocks*, and *Mona Lisa*, which hide symbols of goddess worship and the story of the Magdalene; the Church of Saint-Suplice, which still contains an obelisk, a sign of pagan worship; and tarot cards, which hide themes of pagan mythology. These art objects are constantly viewed by people who see them without seeing their hidden meanings.

Sexism

Sexist men in *The Da Vinci Code* are used as a counterpoint to the religions that celebrates the divine feminine. Fache's inability to accept women in the workplace is one instance of this bias. Another exists in Opus Dei's female devotees, who are not allowed to be in proximity to men and must do their cleaning and other dirty work for no pay. When Teabing reveals himself as the creator of the plot and scorns Sophie as unworthy of possessing the secret of the Grail, his

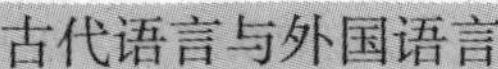

古代语言与外国语言

文中很多隐藏在表象之下的秘密只能通过解读者用语言进行破译。索尼埃给索菲留下有待解码的变形词组，兰登和提彬根据希伯来字母表得出线索，索菲利用镜子帮助他们阅读那段用达·芬奇钟爱的反写字体书写的文字。在《达·芬奇密码》中，语言提示我们秘密无处不在，人们只需对其略加解读，即可发现。

艺术

布朗通过对美术作品的描述证明艺术可以讲述那些历史企图掩盖的故事。这些艺术品包括达·芬奇的《最后的晚餐》、《岩间圣母》和《蒙娜丽莎》，这三幅画中隐藏着女神崇拜象征和玛丽亚·抹大拉的故事；圣叙尔皮斯教堂——其中的方尖碑正是异教崇拜的符号；塔罗纸牌——里面藏有异教神话主题。人们时常遇到这些艺术品，却没能发现其中隐藏的秘密。

男性至上主义

在《达·芬奇密码》中，持性别歧视观点的男性和赞颂神圣女性的宗教相互对应。法希不能接受女性在工作场所出现就是这种偏见的一种表现。另外还表现在天主事工会的女性信徒身上。她们不得接近男性，而且必须无报酬地为他们做清洁工作等脏活。当提彬揭开自己是整个计划策划者的真实面目时，他将索菲贬得一文不值，认为她没资格占有圣杯的秘密。他的

sexism is a sign of his fundamental sourness. In *The Da Vinci Code*, sexist characters are always suspect.

Symbols

Symbols are objects, characters, figures, or colors used to represent abstract ideas or concepts.

Red Hair

Sophie Neveu's red hair, mentioned at the beginning of the text, foreshadows her divine blood. When Langdon first sees Sophie, he calls her hair "burgundy" and thinks that her attractiveness lies in her confidence and health. He compares her favorably to the blonde girls at Harvard over whom his students lust. Later, at Teabing's chateau, Teabing shows Sophie that Mary Magdalene is depicted with red hair in *The Last Supper*. Langdon also thinks the mermaid Ariel's red hair in *The Little Mermaid* is evidence that Disney intended his movie to be an allegory of the story of Magdalene. By the end of the novel, when Sophie's brother gives a tour of the Rosslyn Chapel and his hair is described as "strawberry blonde," we understand that Sophie and her brother are of Mary Magdalene's bloodline.

Blood

Blood stands for truth and enlightenment in *The Da Vinci Code*. Saunière draws a pentacle—for him, a symbol of the Church's intention to cover up the true history of the world—on his stomach in his own blood. Sophie realizes that her

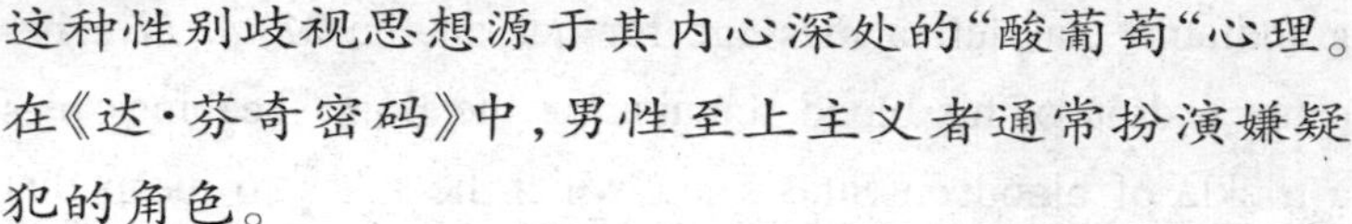

这种性别歧视思想源于其内心深处的“酸葡萄“心理。在《达·芬奇密码》中，男性至上主义者通常扮演嫌疑犯的角色。

象征

象征是用来体现抽象思想或概念的物、人、数字符号或色彩。

红发

小说开篇提到索菲·奈芙的红发，预示了她具有神的血统。兰登初次见到索菲时把她的头发称作勃艮地葡萄酒红，他认为索菲的魅力在于她的自信和健康。他将索菲和哈佛大学中他的学生们迷恋的金发女郎进行比较，对索菲赞许有加。后文中，提彬在城堡里向索菲展示，在《最后的晚餐》中玛丽亚·抹大拉的形象被描绘为有一头红发。兰登也认为在《小美人鱼》一片中，美人鱼阿日耳是迪斯尼意图使本片成为玛丽亚·抹大拉寓言的证据之一。小说结尾，当索菲的弟弟带领他们参观罗斯林教堂时，作者形容他的头发是“草莓般的金红色”，我们由此得知索菲和她的弟弟都具有玛丽亚·抹大拉的血统。

血

在《达·芬奇密码》中，血象征着真理和文明。索尼埃用自己的血在腹部画了一个五角星——对他而言，这是教会意图掩盖世界历史真相的象征。正因为地板

grandfather has left a message for her on the *Mona Lisa* because a drop of his blood remains on the floor. Teabing spies a trickle of blood on Silas's leg, which he takes to mean that Silas has a cilice, a barbed punishment belt, on his thigh, and disables him by hitting him there. Silas himself had thought of blood as truth in a different way—for Silas, blood means cleansing of impurities. And at the very end of the novel, the discovery of the blood of Mary Magdalene running through Sophie and her brother's veins proves that the story of the Grail is true.

Cell Phones

In a novel that spends a great deal of time interpreting ancient symbols like the pentacle, the chalice, and the rose, the cell phone might seem like an incongruous modern interloper. But the cell phone symbolizes the fact that in the modern world, secrets are both harder and easier to keep. Teabing conceals his identity as the Teacher by using cell phones to communicate with his unknowing allies. In one instance, he even speaks to Silas from the back of the limousine while Silas is in the front, concealing his identity while only feet away. At the same time, however, the characters are often worried about their cell phone use being traced. Fache, for example, at one point figures out that Sophie has tipped Langdon off by looking up her phone number, which is stored in his cell phone, and finding that it matches the number Sophie gave Langdon as the American Embassy's number.

上留下了索尼埃的一滴血，索菲才意识到祖父给她在《蒙娜丽莎》上留下了一条信息。提彬发现塞拉斯腿上有一股血流，由此推断塞拉斯穿着粗毛布衣服，大腿上还系着苦修带，于是他就从这下手，将塞拉斯打得不能动弹。塞拉斯则从其他角度将血看作真理——在他看来，流血意味着清除不洁。小说结尾，索菲和弟弟将玛丽亚·抹大拉的血脉传递至今这一发现证明了圣杯故事的真实性。

手机

作者在书中花费大量时间解说诸如五角星、圣餐杯、玫瑰等古代象征符号，手机在这里似乎成了一个不合时宜的现代闯入者。但它却象征一个事实——在现代社会，保守秘密变得更难，抑或更容易。提彬用手机与不知情的盟友联络，隐藏了自己导师的身份。再比如，塞拉斯坐在汽车前排时，提彬却在后排用手机与他通话，仅有咫尺之遥，却隐匿了自己的身份。与此同时，书中人物又经常担忧手机被他人追踪。以法希为例，他查看兰登手机时找到了索菲的电话号码，发现这与索菲给兰登那个所谓美国大使馆的号码一致，由此明白索菲事先给兰登发出过警报。

SUMMARY & ANALYSIS

Prologue–Chapter 3

Summary: Prologue

Jacques Saunière is in the Grand Gallery of the Louvre. He pulls a Caravaggio painting off the wall in order to trigger the gallery's alarm and seal himself inside, away from an albino attacker who is pursuing him. But the protective metal cage does little to stop the man, who pulls a pistol on Saunière and asks him to reveal where "it" is. Saunière at first pretends that he does not know and then gives the albino a false location. The false location is a lie that Saunière has carefully rehearsed. The albino responds that the "others"—three of Saunière's partners—had said the same thing. Then he shoots Saunière in the stomach, says, "Pain is good," and leaves him to die. Saunière realizes that his three partners are dead, and that if he dies, the secret they all shared will die with him. He is desperate to prevent that from happening but realizes he has little time left.

Summary: Chapter 1

Robert Langdon is asleep in his room at the Ritz in Paris when the concierge calls to say he has an important visitor. Langdon, remembering his lecture on religious symbology earlier that night, figures the visitor is some conservative he offended and tells the concierge to send the guest away. Lang-

断章·取义

楔子~第3章

综述:楔子

在卢浮宫的大画廊，为了引发警报系统掩护自己,躲开追杀他的白化病人,雅克·索尼埃从墙上扯下了一幅卡拉瓦乔的画作。但防护金属罩没能阻止此人,他射中了索尼埃,并命令他说出“东西”在哪儿。索尼埃起初假装不知道，随后他告诉了一个错误的位置,这是他操练多次的谎言。白化病人说道,这与其他人也就是索尼埃的三个同伴讲的一模一样。他击中了索尼埃的胃部,并说“疼痛对人有好处”,然后就转身离开了,把索尼埃扔在那里等死。索尼埃意识到三个同伴已死,如果他也死了,大家共同保守的秘密也会一同消亡。他必须想办法避免此事发生,但他明白自己的时间不多了。

综述:第1章

此时罗伯特·兰登正在巴黎丽兹酒店睡觉，酒店接待员打电话说有位重要客人来访。兰登想起当晚早些时候他曾做了一场关于宗教符号学的讲座,他估计此人可能是位被他冒犯的保守人士,于是就让酒店接

don has a history of being controversial—the previous year, he got into an altercation at the Vatican.

After a while, the concierge rings again to let Langdon know the guest is on his way to his room. The visitor, an agent with the French Judicial Police, questions Langdon about his earlier plans to meet with his acquaintance Jacques Saunière for drinks after the lecture. Langdon says that Saunière stood him up. The agent tells Langdon that Saunière is dead and shows him a picture of Saunière's body, which is arranged in a specific way. Langdon is horrified and also afraid—he saw a corpse arranged in a similar way before, and it led to the incident at the Vatican.

SUMMARY & ANALYSIS

Summary: Chapter 2

The albino attacker, Silas, goes to a house that seems to belong to his religious organization, where he has a bedroom. He finds a cell phone in the bottom drawer of the nightstand and calls the Teacher. He tells the Teacher that he has killed Saunière and Saunière's three collaborators, and that each of them named the Church of Saint-Suplice as the secret resting place for the keystone that he and the Teacher and their comrades seek. The Teacher tells Silas to go to Saint-Suplice immediately and retrieve the keystone. Before obeying, Silas engages in some "corporal mortification," a masochistic practice of physical self-punishment, as a way of doing penance for sins. Silas tightens the barbed cilice, a punishment belt, around his thigh, and flagellates himself, all the while repeating his mantra: "Pain is good."

待员把客人请走。去年他曾在梵蒂冈卷入了一场争论,因而一度引起争议。

不一会儿,酒店接待员再次给兰登打电话,说客人正在去他房间的路上。来访者是位法国司法警察,他询问兰登有关与索尼埃约定在讲座后见面小酌一事。兰登说索尼埃并没有赴约。警察告诉兰登索尼埃被人谋杀了,并给他看了一张照片,上边索尼埃的尸体摆成了一种特别的姿势。兰登非常震惊,他之前也看过一张类似的尸体照片,随后梵蒂冈就发生了一起暴力事件。

综述:第2章

袭击索尼埃的白化病人塞拉斯正一瘸一拐地走入一栋看上去属于他那个宗教组织的房子,他在那儿有个房间。他从床头衣柜最底部的抽屉里找到手机,然后拨通了导师的电话,告诉导师他已经杀死了索尼埃和他的三个同伴,每个人都确定导师及其同伴们搜寻的楔石就在圣叙尔皮斯教堂。导师命令塞拉斯立即前往圣叙尔皮斯教堂取回楔石。出发之前,塞拉斯实施了"肉体苦行"仪式,信徒们通过这种自虐式的肉体惩罚进行苦修来去除罪孽。他系紧扎身的粗布衣服和大腿上的苦修带,然后开始鞭笞自己,这一切都是在重复他虔信的咒语:"疼痛对人有好处"。

Summary: Chapter 3

Langdon leaves the hotel, and Jerome Collet, an agent of the French Judicial Police, drives him across Paris to the Louvre. In the car Langdon muses about the history of some of Paris's famous architecture. He wishes he could be with his former flame, Vittoria, on the Eiffel Tower, a structure he mocks as a reflection of the culture's machismo. Collet drops him off by the glass pyramid, the entrance to the museum designed by I.M. Pei. Inside, Langdon meets Bezu Fache, the police captain nicknamed "the Bull."

Analysis: Prologue–Chapter 3

Saunière's murder is an instigating moment in the story. By setting it in an art gallery, a place not normally associated with drama or intrigue, Brown indicates to the reader that his novel will take an unusual approach toward art. As a museum curator, Saunière is respectful of art. When he commits vandalism by ripping the Caravaggio off the wall, it symbolizes that the story will undo many of our assumptions about the sacred nature of high art. This act of vandalism also shows the lengths to which Saunière will to go to survive. Saunière is not, however, willing to give up his secret, even if his reticence means death. The reader may suspect that this secret has some connection to artwork, since the opening scene is set in a museum, but aside from that clue the nature of the secret is unknown. Its discovery will occupy much of the novel.

Langdon is the perfect man to uncover Saunière's secret. On one hand, he is like the reader—clueless about what is going on and why. On the other hand, as a professor of symbology, he is very knowledgeable and well equipped to solve the

综述:第3章

法国司法警察杰罗姆·科莱驾车带兰登驶过巴黎前往卢浮宫。在车上,兰登思索着巴黎那些著名建筑的历史。他多希望此刻能和前任女友维多利亚一起登上埃菲尔铁塔——他曾取笑它是法国文化中男子气概的反映。科莱将他送到由贝聿铭设计的博物馆入口——玻璃金字塔,在那儿他遇到了绰号为“公牛”的警察局长贝祖·法希。

品评:楔子~第3章

索尼埃被谋杀这一事件拉开了故事的序幕。布朗通过将这一场景设置在美术馆——一个通常与紧张刺激或阴谋诡计无关的地方——由此向读者表明他的小说将会以不同寻常的手法描写艺术话题。作为博物馆馆长,索尼埃非常尊重艺术。但他野蛮地把卡拉瓦乔的画作从墙上拽下来的行为,意味着这个故事将颠覆很多我们对于高雅艺术神圣本质的先入之见。这一行为也体现了索尼埃为求生付出的巨大努力。即使沉默对他来说意味着死亡,他也不愿吐露秘密。由于故事开篇发生在博物馆里,所以读者很可能会怀疑秘密与艺术品有关。但除了这条线索之外,我们对秘密的性质一无所知,因此全书大部分篇幅将会与发现秘密有关。

兰登是揭开索尼埃秘密的最佳人选。一方面,他同读者一样,对即将发生的事情及它为何发生毫无头绪;另一方面,作为象征学教授,他知识广博,足以破

mystery. It seems that most of Langdon's knowledge has been academic, with no real-life application. Here, he is given a chance to apply his puzzle-solving skills to an actual murder.

Silas is a masochist who lives by the motto "pain is good." Pain is also at the foundation of his religious beliefs. Silas is a sinister representative of his religious group. His violent behavior, whether directed toward himself—the cilice belt, the self-flagellation—or toward others, as exemplified by his willingness to murder, makes his organization seem evil. Although what the philosophy "pain is good" has to do with the goals of the Teacher, and why Saunière was working against this group, is not yet known, the reader does know that Silas and his organization are threatening.

Langdon displays a wry sense of humor, especially in his musings on French culture. His academic specialty affects his outlook: he seems to see the world around him in terms of symbols. For example, his discussion of French culture arises from an analysis of its architecture and the Freudian symbols he perceives in its architecture. This way of perceiving the world may be helpful for solving Saunière's murder, but it is also a limited method of perception.

Chapters 4–9

Summary: Chapter 4

Fache leads Langdon through the darkened Louvre to the Grand Gallery, where Saunière's body lies. Saunière is revealed to have been a connoisseur of goddess iconography—relics related to religions that worship the sacred feminine—and that Langdon is writing a book on the same subject. Lang-

解谜团。看上去兰登掌握的多是书本知识,没怎么用到现实生活当中,但作者在这里给了他一个机会——用自己的解密技巧去侦破一起真实发生的谋杀案。

塞拉斯是一个把“疼痛对人有好处”当作生活信条的自虐狂,疼痛是他宗教信仰的基石。塞拉斯是他所属宗教团体的邪恶代表。不论是针对他自己的,诸如苦修带和自我鞭笞此类的暴力行为,还是由他的谋杀欲望所体现出来的对别人的暴力行为,都使得他所属的宗教团体看起来无比邪恶。尽管“疼痛对人有好处”这种生活哲学与导师的目的有关,而且读者依然不知道索尼埃为何反对这个团体,但我们可以清楚地看到塞拉斯和他那个组织已形成了一定威胁。

兰登对四周环境进行了一番揶揄,这在他对法国文化进行沉思时尤为明显。专业特长影响了他的看法,他似乎习惯了以象征符号来观察周围的世界。例如,兰登对法国文化的探讨就起源于他对其建筑中弗洛伊德式象征符号的理解以及对法国建筑的分析。这种观察世界的方式或许有助于侦破索尼埃谋杀案,但它也会使他的理解方法受到局限。

第4~9章

综述:第4章

法希带领兰登穿过黑暗的卢浮宫,走进大画廊,索尼埃的尸体就躺在那里。索尼埃被看作是女神图像符号学的鉴定家,那是有关崇拜神圣女性宗教的一些遗物,它与兰登正在写的书涉及同一主题。这本书现

don's book has been kept a secret because he believes that some of his interpretations will be controversial. Fache seems unpleasant and fairly hostile. Langdon notices that the police inspector is wearing a crux gemmata, a religious pin depicting Jesus and his twelve apostles.

Saunière's body is surrounded by a metal barricade, part of "containment security," a measure used by the museum to try to trap thieves on the premises. Fache makes Langdon climb under the barricade with him, and Langdon clumsily bangs his head.

Summary: Chapter 5

Bishop Manuel Aringarosa, the president-general of Opus Dei, packs his bags and leaves his organization's luxurious headquarters in New York City to board a plane headed for Rome. Though he is dressed modestly, he wears an elaborate bishop's ring. While in the air, Aringarosa reflects on the history of Opus Dei, a conservative Catholic organization started early in the twentieth century. Lately Opus Dei has been besieged by critics who say that the organization is a religious cult. But as of five months ago, the biggest threat to the organization wasn't coming from the media or from the organization's critics, but from a different source, one not yet revealed to the reader. While in the air, Aringarosa takes a phone call from someone who reports Silas's discovery that the keystone is hidden in the Church of Saint-Suplice. The Bishop agrees to pull some strings to gain Silas access to the church. Meanwhile, Silas is preparing to retrieve the keystone. He is excited about this mission in a way he hasn't been since joining the church. His excitement makes his violent past come flooding back to him.

在还处于保密之中，因为兰登认为书中的某些非传统解析将会引起争议。法希好像十分不悦，而且带有很强的敌意。兰登注意到这位局长戴着宝石十字架——一个带有宗教意味、象征耶稣与十二门徒的领带夹。

索尼埃的尸体被隔在一道金属栅栏里面，它是“封闭保护”装置的一部分。博物馆采取这种措施把窃贼关在馆中。法希让兰登随他从栅栏下面爬进去，兰登笨手笨脚磕到了自己的脑袋。

综述：第5章

天主事工会总会长曼努埃尔·阿林加洛沙已经打好行装，准备离开这一组织位于纽约市的豪华总部，乘飞机前往罗马。尽管穿着俭朴，但他仍然戴着精工制作的主教戒指。在飞机上，阿林加洛沙回忆起天主事工会这一创始于20世纪初的保守天主教组织的历史。近来天主事工会受到人们围攻，批评者称这一组织是个邪教。但在5个月前，一种比媒体和批评者们更强大的威胁向天主事工会袭来，读者们尚未知晓它的来源。阿林加洛沙在飞机上接了一个电话，打电话的人说塞拉斯已经发现楔石藏在圣叙尔皮斯教堂。主教同意利用私人关系让塞拉斯进入教堂。与此同时，塞拉斯正准备取回楔石。想到这次使命，他感到十分激动，这是他加入教会以来从未有过的。兴奋之情使他那充满暴力色彩的过去再次涌进他的脑海。

Summary: Chapter 6

Standing in front of Saunière's body, Langdon explains to Fache the significance of the way Saunière arranged himself before dying. The curator drew a pentacle on his stomach with his own blood. The pentacle, a five-pointed star that symbolizes the pagan goddess Venus, has often been misinterpreted as a sign of devil worship. Fache shows Langdon that Saunière is clutching a glow-in-the-dark marker that the museum staff uses to make maintenance notes on paintings. With the help of a black light, a message is revealed. Fache asks Langdon to help him understand it. Meanwhile, Collet is taping this conversation from Saunière's former office.

Summary: Chapter 7

Sister Sandrine, the keeper of the Church of Saint-Suplice, is awakened in the middle of the night by a phone call from her boss, who tells her that Aringarosa asked him to let a member of Opus Dei come to the church immediately. She is taken aback by this request, but she does as her boss asks. Sandrine, a pious woman, does as her superiors ask. Still, she is mistrustful of Opus Dei. She is disturbed by the sect's practice of "corporal mortification," or physical self-punishment, and she disapproves of their discrimination toward women.

Summary: Chapter 8

As Collet continues to survey the scene from afar, Langdon takes in the cryptic message that Saunière has written next to his body:

"13–3–2–21–1–1–8–5

O, Draconian devil!

综述:第6章

兰登站在索尼埃尸体前,向法希解释索尼埃在临死前把身体摆成这个样子具有重大意义。馆长用自己的血在腹部画了个五角星。这一象征异教女神维纳斯的五角星,即带有五个角的星形,曾被误以为是魔鬼崇拜的符号。法希给兰登看了索尼埃手中紧握的一只黑光笔,博物馆工作人员通常使用这种笔在画作上留下维护标记。一条信息在黑光灯下显露出来,法希要求兰登帮他破解。与此同时,科莱正在索尼埃办公室将两人的谈话录了下来。

综述:第7章

子夜时分,一个电话吵醒了圣叙尔皮斯教堂的看守——修女桑德琳·比埃尔。院长在电话中告诉她,阿林加洛沙要求让一名天主事工会僧侣马上进入教堂。她对这个要求感到迷惑不解,但还是按院长的吩咐把那人放了进来。作为一个虔诚的女人,桑德琳遵从了修道院院长的命令,但她并不信任天主事工会。这个教派实行的“肉体苦行”,即自我体罚令她感到不安。此外,她也不赞成天主事工会对妇女的歧视性做法。

综述:第8章

当科莱继续向远处搜寻犯罪现场时,兰登读懂了索尼埃留在自己身体旁的密码信息:

“13-3-2-21-1-1-8-5

啊,严酷的魔王!

Oh, lame saint! "

Langdon is confused by the code's contents and by the fact that it is written in English and not French, Saunière's maiden tongue. With the help of a black light, Fache reveals that Saunière has also drawn a circle around his naked body with invisible ink. The way his nude body is splayed within the circle suggests Da Vinci's famous drawing, *The Vitruvian Man*. Fache interprets the symbol as a reference to devil worship. Da Vinci had a complicated relationship with the church and included subversive codes or elements even in the religious paintings he was commissioned to create.

In his office, Collet eavesdrops on Fache's and Langdon's conversation using audio equipment. Collet reflects on Fache's devotion to the Catholic Church and on the amazing instincts with which he solves crimes. Apparently, prior to Langdon's arrival, Fache announced to his men that he thought he knew the identity of Saunière's killer. In addition to monitoring the audio equipment, Collet is monitoring the GPS tracking system.

Summary: Chapter 9

Sophie Neveu shows up at the Grand Gallery claiming that she has deciphered the code. Fache, who turned off his phone and told Collet not to let anyone in, is angered by this interruption. He is particularly annoyed at being interrupted by Neveu, because he does not think that women should be allowed to do police work. He considers them physically weak and distracting to men.

As soon as Sophie arrives, she gives Langdon a message to call the U.S. Embassy, which has been trying to contact him with news. However, Langdon discovers that the number she

噢,瘸腿的圣徒!”

密码的内容让兰登迷惑不解,而且他也不明白索尼埃为何不用母语法语,而是用英语写下这一密码。借助黑光灯,法希向兰登展示除此之外索尼埃还用显隐墨水在自己的裸体四周划了个圆圈。圆圈之内,他裸体伸展的方式正与达·芬奇的名画《维特鲁威人》相符。法希认为这一符号涉及到魔鬼崇拜。达·芬奇与教会关系错综复杂,他甚至还在教会委托他绘制的画作中绘上了某些具有颠覆性的代码和元素。

科莱此时在办公室通过音频设备监听法希与兰登谈话,并想着法希那虔诚的天主教信仰和神奇的破案本能。很明显,在兰登到来之前,法希就已经向手下宣称他知道是谁杀了索尼埃。除了使用音频设备监听之外,科莱还动用了全球定位追踪系统。

综述:第9章

索菲·奈芙出现在大画廊,她说自己已破译了密码。法希之前已关掉手机,并吩咐科莱不要放任何人进来,因此他对有人闯进来愤怒不已。尤其令他恼火的是闯入者是奈芙,法希认为不应允许女性出现在工作场所,因为她们不仅体力较弱而且会令男性分心。

索菲一到就捎信给兰登,让他给美国大使馆去电话,那边有事要与他联系。然而兰登发现索菲给他的

has given him is not the U.S. Embassy at all, but Sophie's own answering service with a recording telling him that he is in trouble.

Analysis: Chapters 4–9

The narrative structure of *The Da Vinci Code* allows the reader to put together clues alongside Langdon and the police investigating Saunière's murder. At this point, the clue about Saunière's secret involving the "sacred feminine" remains to be solved. The account Langdon gives of it is not thorough, and Langdon himself does not understand how the written message relates to the theory of the sacred feminine. What is clear is that Langdon has unwittingly gotten involved in the conspiracy.

It's also clear that although Sophie does not specify the source of danger, it is related to Fache and his men. Brown casts suspicion on Fache not only by making him unpleasant and sexist, but also by linking him to the Catholic Church. Thus far, Brown has portrayed the members of Opus Dei unfavorably. In his description of the headquarters of Opus Dei and of the Bishop's penthouse apartment and elaborate ring, Brown associates luxury and worldly goods with a sinister force. The Bishop's amethyst and diamond ring contrasts with his own description of Opus Dei as a society dedicated to helping people live their lives in service to the Catholic Church. By juxtaposing the group's declared intentions with its luxurious trappings, Brown suggests that Opus Dei is not necessarily interested only in spiritual wealth.

Sister Sandrine embodies the Catholic Church's passive attitude toward the Opus Dei sect. Although Sister Sandrine is pious and godly, and although she has suspicions about Opus

号码根本不是美国大使馆的电话，而是索菲自己的电话留言，里面有条录音通知他已身处困境。

品评：第4~9章

《达·芬奇密码》的叙事结构使得读者可将有关兰登和警方调查索尼埃谋杀案的线索汇总起来。在这一点上，索尼埃有关"神圣女性"的秘密仍有待破解。兰登对此做出的描述并不完整，他也不明白为何留言会与神圣女性的理论存在关联。唯一清楚的是兰登在无意之中卷入了这起阴谋。

同样明显的一点是索菲没有指明危险来自何方，但它可能与法希和其属下有关。布朗将法希描绘成令人不快的男性至上主义者，还与天主教廷有所联系，由此为他涂上了嫌疑犯的色彩。至此，在布朗笔下，天主事工会的成员们都不讨人喜欢。他通过描述天主事工会总部、主教的顶楼套房和他精工细制的戒指，将奢侈世俗之物同某种凶险的力量联系起来。主教的紫水晶钻戒同他自己对天主事工会的描述形成了鲜明的对比：在他的描绘中，天主事工会是致力于帮助人们为天主教会服务的社团。但布朗却将这一组织所宣称的意图同它那些奢侈的装饰并举，暗示读者天主事工会并非只关心精神财富。

修女桑德琳·比埃尔象征着天主教会中对天主事工会持否定态度的一方。尽管她信仰虔诚，崇敬上帝，

Dei, she feels she cannot call the sect into question because the Pope himself has sanctioned the organization. However much she may worry, she will do whatever her boss asks because she considers unquestioning obedience part of her faith and duty.

Brown tackles the issue of sexism in this chapter by explaining Fache's attitude toward Sophie Neveu. Fache seems threatened by Sophie's education and self-possessed attitude. Fache's annoyance at Sophie's arrival at the crime scene and the message she has left for Langdon suggests that he plans to put Langdon in danger. It also raises questions about the detective's connection to Opus Dei.

Chapters 10–15

Summary: Chapter 10

As Silas arrives at Saint-Suplice, he reflects on his past. He ran away from home at a young age after murdering his abusive father and continued to live a life of violence. He was in prison for murder when an earthquake opened a big hole in the wall of his cell. When he ran, he ended up at a church in Oviedo, Spain. Aringarosa, then a missionary, saved him and gave him the name Silas, after a passage in the Bible. From that point on Silas became deeply devout. He is now Aringarosa's faithful righthand man.

On the plane, Bishop Aringarosa thinks about how Opus Dei offered the Teacher a large amount of money for information about the location of the keystone. The Teacher told Aringarosa that he must not be in contact with Silas, presumably in order to maintain secrecy and throw the police off the scent.

并且对天主事工会心存怀疑，但因为教皇本人认可这个组织，她也不敢对此提出质疑。虽然疑虑重重，但她仍按院长的吩咐去做，因为在她看来，毫不犹豫地服从已成为信仰与义务的一部分。

布朗在本章通过描写法希对索菲的态度探讨了性别歧视问题。索菲所受的教育和她沉着镇定的态度似乎使法希感到受到了威胁。法希对索菲来到犯罪现场表现出的恼怒，以及索菲给兰登的留言都在暗示他意图让兰登陷入困境，这不禁让读者对这位侦探与天主事工会有怎样的联系产生了疑问。

第 10~15 章

综述：第 10 章

抵达圣叙尔皮斯教堂时，塞拉斯还沉浸在回忆当中。年少时他杀死了暴戾的父亲，然后离家出走，过上了充满暴力的生活。在因谋杀罪被判入狱后，一场地震将他所在牢房的墙壁震出了一个大洞。他的逃亡之旅终止在西班牙奥维耶多的一座教堂，传教士阿林加洛沙救了他，并根据圣经中的某个章节给他起名为塞拉斯。从那时起，塞拉斯就成了一位极度虔诚的信徒，如今他是阿林加洛沙忠实可靠的得力助手。

在飞机上，阿林加洛沙主教正考虑天主事工会为获知楔石位置会如何向导师支付巨额酬金。导师告诉阿林加洛沙他绝不能与塞拉斯联络，这大概是为了保守秘密，摆脱警方追踪。

Summary: Chapter 11

As Langdon listens to Sophie's message, Sophie tells Fache that if put in ascending order, the numbers next to Saunière's body form the Fibonacci sequence, a progression in which each term is equal to the sum of the two preceding terms. If Sophie is right, the code was a cryptographic joke. Unsatisfied with Sophie's interpretation, Fache grows even angrier. Sophie leaves, and Langdon tells Fache that according to the embassy, a friend has had an accident. Langdon goes to the restroom after saying he isn't feeling well and would like to be alone. Collet and Fache track him electronically. Fache tells Collet to make sure Langdon doesn't leave the gallery.

Summary: Chapter 12

Sophie meets Langdon in the bathroom to explain her message further. She tells him that he is a suspect, and that a GPS tracker has been planted on him. After rummaging in his pocket, Langdon finds a tracker and realizes it must have been planted on him at the hotel. Langdon's first impulse is to throw the tracker away, but Sophie convinces him that a static dot on the tracking screen would immediately arouse police suspicion. She shows him a picture of the crime scene that Fache uploaded to her departmental website. Fache photographed a line and then erased before Langdon's arrival, but the line is visible in the picture. It reads, "P.S. Find Robert Langdon."

Summary: Chapter 13

Sophie tells Langdon that the police have more than enough evidence to arrest him for the murder, but she knows

综述:第 11 章

趁兰登听留言的时候,索菲告诉法希若将索尼埃身边数字以升序排列,即可构成斐波那契数列,数列中每一项等于前面两项之和。假如她猜的没错,这列数码是一个密码游戏。法希对索菲的解释并不满意,反而大为恼火。索菲离开后,兰登说大使馆通知他有位朋友出了点事情,他感到身体有些不适,想独自呆一会儿,随后他去了洗手间。法希和科莱对兰登进行了电子跟踪,法希叮嘱科莱务必保证兰登不离开画廊。

综述:第 12 章

索菲在洗手间里与兰登碰头,她进一步解释了留言的目的。她告诉兰登他已经成了嫌疑犯,而且身上还装有全球定位跟踪装置。兰登在口袋里搜寻一番,果然找着了跟踪装置,他意识到这一定是在宾馆时警方装在他身上的。兰登的第一个念头是扔掉跟踪装置,但索菲说如果扔掉它,跟踪屏幕上的信号就会固定不动,警方就会立即产生怀疑。她给兰登看了一张法希在犯罪现场拍摄并上传到她所属部门网站的图片,法希在兰登到来之前拍到了一行文字,然后又把它擦去,图片上是一行清晰的文字,写着“附言:找到罗伯特·兰登”。

综述:第 13 章

索菲告诉兰登,警方已经掌握了充足的证据要以

that he is innocent. She believes Saunière was telling her to look for him. Saunière knew that *The Vitruvian Man* was her favorite Da Vinci drawing. He also must have known that if he put numbers into the message on the floor, the cryptography department would get involved with the investigation. Also, she thinks that the "P.S." in the message "P.S. Find Robert Langdon" stands for Princesse Sophie, his nickname for her. Langdon is confused about Sophie's connection to Saunière. He suspects that Sophie may have been Saunière's mistress until she tells him that Saunière was her grandfather, but that they'd had a falling-out.

Summary: Chapter 14

Ten minutes have gone by. Fache and Collet wonder why Langdon has not returned from the bathroom. Collet tells Fache that Langdon is not onto their plan. The tracking dot is showing slight movements, indicating that it is still on his body. If Langdon had found the device, he would have removed it and tried to run.

Collet thinks that Fache is unusually invested in this case, probably because Fache has recently suffered a some bad public relations and needs a high-profile arrest to secure his position. The director of the cryptology department calls. He wants to talk to Fache about Sophie Neveu.

Summary: Chapter 15

Silas moves toward the Church of Saint-Suplice. He sees some teenage prostitutes on the plaza. The lust he feels is immediately smothered by the pain of the punishment belt around his thigh. Silas has taken a vow of celibacy for Opus

谋杀罪逮捕他，但她相信他是无辜的。她确信索尼埃是想让她去寻找兰登，因为索尼埃知道《维特鲁威人》是达·芬奇画作中她最喜爱的一幅，他也一定知道假若在地板上留下数字信息，密码部门必定会介入调查。此外，索菲认为在留言“附言：找到罗伯特·兰登”中的“附言”(P.S.)是指她的昵称索菲公主(Princess Sophie)。兰登对索菲与索尼埃的关系感到困惑，他怀疑索菲可能是索尼埃的情妇，索菲告诉他她是索尼埃的孙女，但他们曾经发生过争吵。

综述：第14章

10分钟过去了，兰登还没从洗手间出来，法希和科莱感到莫名其妙。科莱对法希说兰登并不知道他们的计划，跟踪信号存在轻微移动说明这一装置还在他身上。倘如兰登有所察觉，一定会扔掉它试图逃跑。

科莱觉得法希投入精力侦办此案不同寻常，这大概与法希最近糟糕的公众形象有关，他需要来一次高调的拘捕行动来巩固地位。这时密码部主任打来电话，要与法希谈谈索菲的事。

综述：第15章

塞拉斯向圣叙尔皮斯教堂走去，广场上一些十几岁的妓女激起了他的肉欲，但大腿上苦修带的疼痛立即压灭了这种欲望。他曾在天主事工会立下禁欲誓

Dei, a vow he sees as a small price to pay for salvation, especially considering the sexual assault he endured in prison. Prepared to retrieve the keystone, he knocks on the door of the church.

Analysis: Chapters 10–15

Silas's conversion to Christianity sprung from his first experience of kindness. Aringarosa was willing to shelter and care for Silas despite Silas's dark past. Such unconditional support, so new to Silas, has made Silas devoted to Aringarosa and willing to believe everything Aringarosa tells him. Silas seems totally willing to return to his violent tendencies, this time under the pretext of religion and furthering Opus Dei. At this point, it is not entirely clear whether Aringarosa is taking advantage of Silas to further his own plans.

Fache's connection to Opus Dei is unclear. He is a pious Catholic who has been known to mix church and state affairs, and Brown makes us wonder whether he is in on the keystone conspiracy. On one hand, Fache genuinely seems to believe that Langdon is guilty of Saunière's murder. On the other hand, it is possible that Fache's seeming belief is actually just an act for Collet's sake, and that Fache is setting Langdon up.

Like Opus Dei, Fache is prejudiced toward women. His contempt for women works to his disadvantage—by underestimating Sophie's intelligence, he allows himself to be tricked. It seems obvious that Sophie is up to something, but Brown means for the reader to believe that the strength of Fache's prejudice prevents him from seeing what is actually going on.

The strength of Sophie's faith in Langdon's innocence is slightly puzzling, but it might simply be a reflection of her

言,尤其是考虑到他在狱中忍受的强暴,这一誓言在他眼中不过是为了灵魂拯救而付出的微小代价。做好了找回楔石的准备后,他叩响了教堂的大门。

品评:第10~15章

塞拉斯皈依天主源于早年那段美好的经历。尽管知道他的过去并不光彩,阿林加洛沙依然无条件地支持他,庇护他。这一切对他是如此新鲜,以至于他全心全意忠实于主教,相信他的每一句话。在宗教甚至是天主事工会的名义下,塞拉斯好像十分愿意重操往日的暴力本行。此时读者尚不清楚,阿林加洛沙是否会利用塞拉斯来进一步实施他的计划。

法希与天主事工会的关系模糊不清。身为虔诚的天主教徒,他经常将教会与国家事务混为一谈,布朗由此让读者对法希是否参与寻找楔石的阴谋产生了怀疑。一方面,法希似乎确定是兰登谋杀了索尼埃;但另一方面,法希看似合理的想法很可能只是要给科莱做个样子,他实际上是想让兰登协助他侦破此案。

与天主事工会类似,法希也对女性抱有偏见。轻视女性是他工作中的弱点,正因他低估了索菲的智力,才使自己上当受骗。很明显,索菲可以胜任某些工作,但布朗却想让读者相信,法希这一偏见的力量使他无法看清事态的发展。

索菲为何坚信兰登是无辜的让人迷惑不解,这可能是索菲良好本能的一种反映。两人一同踏上发现之

good instincts. The dynamic between Sophie and Langdon will be one of the driving interpersonal forces of the novel as both of them embark on a mission of discovery. If Sophie is right that Saunière wrote the code and message in order to bring her and Langdon together, it must be because Saunière thought that together the pair could uncover his secret.

Chapters 16–20

Summary: Chapter 16

Sophie thinks about the phone message she got from Saunière earlier that day. She and Saunière were estranged for over a decade after she saw him engaged in an act she found despicable. He wrote her letters and tried to explain what she had seen, but Sophie refused to have any contact with him.

The message Sophie got from Saunière sounded urgent. In it, he said they were both in danger, and he had to tell her the truth about what happened to her family. Sophie's family died in a car accident when she was little. She thought her grandfather's message was just a ploy to get her to talk to him. She did not call him back.

Sophie asks Langdon to explain why Saunière would want to meet with him, but he doesn't know. She tries to convince Langdon to leave the museum with her and go to the American Embassy for protection while they figure out what happened to her grandfather. Langdon refuses to run. Fache calls Sophie's cell phone, but she turns it off. Sophie looks out the window and wonders whether Langdon could make it out of the building by jumping.

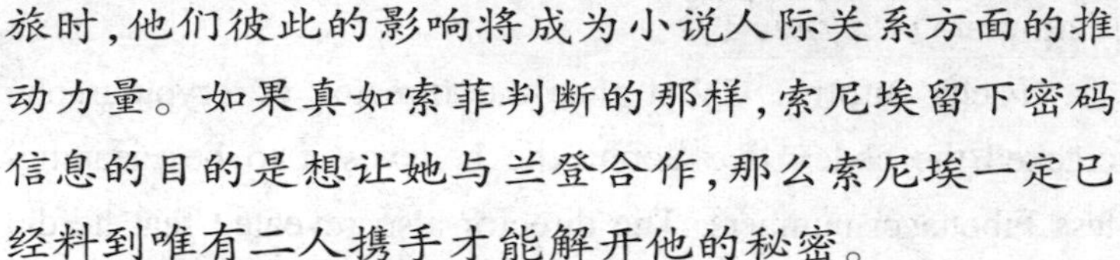

旅时,他们彼此的影响将成为小说人际关系方面的推动力量。如果真如索菲判断的那样,索尼埃留下密码信息的目的是想让她与兰登合作,那么索尼埃一定已经料到唯有二人携手才能解开他的秘密。

第16~20章

综述:第16章

索菲想起那天早些时候索尼埃给她的电话留言。自从看到索尼埃参与一项令她无法接受的可鄙行为后,他们的关系就疏远了。索尼埃曾写信向她解释当时的事情,但十多年来索菲一直拒绝与他有任何联系。

索尼埃给索菲的留言听起来很紧急,他说他和索菲的处境都很危险,因此不得不告诉她有关她家庭的事实真相。在索菲小时候,她的家人死于一场车祸。她以为祖父的留言不过是为了让她重新和他交谈的伎俩,所以没有回电。

索菲要求兰登解释索尼埃为何要与他会面,但兰登也并不清楚。当两人弄清她祖父的状况后,索菲劝兰登离开博物馆去美国大使馆寻求保护,但兰登拒绝逃跑。法希拨打索菲手机,她却关机了。索菲朝窗外望去,琢磨着兰登能否跳窗逃脱。

Summary: Chapter 17

Fache informs Collet that the director of cryptography cracked the code—like Sophie, he believes it to be meaningless Fibonacci numbers. The director also revealed that he did not send Sophie over to the museum, and that Saunière was Sophie's grandfather. Collet, like Sophie, believes that Saunière must have written the code in order to get his granddaughter involved in the case.

Fache and Collet continue to try to reach Sophie. An alarm rings, signaling a security breach in the men's room. The two policemen see on the GPS screen that Langdon has apparently jumped out of the window.

Summary: Chapter 18

Collet sees the tracking dot go out of the window and then come to a complete stop. The police assume Langdon has committed suicide, but then the dot starts moving away from the building and down the road. Fache looks out the bathroom window and sees a huge flatbed truck moving away. Assuming that Langdon must have jumped onto the truck, Fache runs out of the building to apprehend him.

Meanwhile, Sophie and Langdon hide in the shadows of the museum. The narrator explains that Sophie broke the window using a garbage can and then threw the GPS tracker, which she had imbedded in a bar of soap, out the window and onto the truck. Once all of the police have left the building, Sophie tells Langdon to go down a side stairwell with her. Langdon is impressed with Sophie's quick thinking.

综述:第17章

法希通知科莱密码部主任已破译密码——和索菲一样，他也相信这不过是毫无意义的斐波那契数列。主任同时表明他并没有派索菲去博物馆，索菲其实是索尼埃的孙女。和索菲一样，科莱也觉得索尼埃留下密码一定是想让孙女牵涉到此案中来。

法希和科莱继续寻找索菲，这时警报器响了起来，提示男洗手间安全系统发出了信号。两名警察看着全球定位监视屏幕，吃惊地发现兰登已经跃出窗外。

综述:第18章

科莱看到跟踪信号来到窗外，然后完全静止不动了。警方推测兰登已经自杀，但追踪信号又开始在楼外移动，并沿着马路前进。法希透过洗手间窗户看到一辆巨型平板卡车正驶离博物馆，他估量兰登一定跳上了卡车，于是警察们跑出楼外去抓兰登。

与此同时，索菲和兰登还藏在博物馆阴暗的角落里。作者随后揭示，索菲用垃圾桶砸破窗户，然后把全球定位跟踪装置埋在肥皂里，扔到了窗外停靠的卡车上。所有警察一离开大楼，索菲便带领兰登沿侧面的楼梯井下楼。兰登对她的敏捷思维钦佩不已。

Summary: Chapter 19

Silas enters Saint-Suplice. Sister Sandrine offers to give him a tour of the church, but he refuses it. He asks her to go back to bed, saying he wants to pray and can show himself around. She agrees, but she is suspicious of him. Hiding in the shadows, she watches him pray, thinking that Silas might be the enemy she was warned about.

Summary: Chapter 20

As he tries to decipher Saunière's message, Langdon realizes that everything in the message relates in some way to PHI, or 1.618, the number of Divine Proportion, starting with the Fibonacci sequence. He thinks of a lecture he gives about how PHI is the numerical proportion of many things in nature and in art, including the pentacle, the symbol of the sacred feminine.

Suddenly, Langdon realizes that the word portion of Saunière's message is actually an anagram. He unscrambles it and gets: "Leonardo Da Vinci! The Mona Lisa!"

Analysis: Chapters 16–20

It is not surprising that Saunière would want to bring Sophie and Langdon together—as Brown demonstrates in this chapter, they make an effective team. Unlike the many sexist characters that populate the novel, such as Fache, Langdon clearly respects women. When Sophie figures out how to trick the police by embedding the tracking advice in a bar of soap and throwing it out the window, Langdon is humbled and impressed by her cleverness and quick thinking. But Langdon is not simply looking on in wonder; he pulls his own weight,

综述:第 19 章

塞拉斯走进圣叙尔皮斯教堂,桑德琳嬷嬷要领他参观教堂,被他拒绝了。他让嬷嬷回去休息,他说他只想做做祈祷,然后再四处转转。嬷嬷同意了,但却对他产生了怀疑。她藏在阴影里,看着他做祈祷,她想塞拉斯可能就是警告中的敌人。

综述:第 20 章

兰登试图破译索尼埃的密码信息,他意识到自斐波那契数列开始,密码中的一切在某个方面都和黄金分割率 PHI,也就是 1.618 这一数字存在联系。他想起自己曾在课上解释过 PHI 为什么在自然界和艺术中随处可见,其中就包括象征神圣女性的五角星。

兰登突然发现索尼埃密码信息的文字部分是个字谜,可以解读为"列奥纳多·达·芬奇!蒙娜丽莎!"

品评:第 16~20 章

索尼埃想让索菲和兰登合作并不令人奇怪,正如布朗在本章节所述,他们俩可以组成一个高效的团队。和小说中诸如法希之类的众多大男子主义者不同,兰登显然是个尊重女性的人。索菲能想到把跟踪装置埋到肥皂里,扔出窗外来糊弄警方,兰登却是笨手笨脚,只能折服于她的聪慧和机敏。但兰登绝不仅是个只会惊讶的旁观者;他恪尽职责,破解了令索菲和密码部其他同事都束手无策的密码。兰登是位学者

breaking the code that neither Sophie nor anyone in her cryptography department could solve. Langdon is an academic and extremely book-smart, while Sophie is the one with the street smarts. She can think on her feet and wriggle out of difficult situations.

Brown introduces his characters' backgrounds without breaking the narrative thread. By revealing that Sophie was not in contact with her grandfather because she was traumatized by something she witnessed him doing, Brown intentionally creates confusion. The novel is structured to make us sympathetic toward Saunière, the victim, but on the other hand, Sophie's anger with him forces us to question his integrity.

Collet represents the neutral observer. He does not seem to have any ulterior motives, and unlike Fache, he has no personal investment in the case. Brown still has not revealed whether Fache's interest in the job is motivated by the desire for a high profile case to secure his position, as Collett believes, or by a connection with the Opus Dei.

Chapters 21–25

Summary: Chapter 21

Sophie remembers that her grandfather liked to create anagrams of famous paintings. When she was young, he took her to visit the *Mona Lisa* when the museum was closed. She did not think much of the painting at the time. She realizes that the *Mona Lisa* would be a good place for him to leave her a message, and that he would have been able to visit the painting before he died. Sophie decides to go back up the stairwell to find the painting. She tells Langdon to go to the

兼理论天才,而索菲则是白手起家的实践能手。身处逆境,她能脚踏实地,另辟蹊径。

布朗一边继续阐述叙事线索,一边交待出人物背景。他通过介绍索菲不和祖父联络,是由于她目击祖父做了某件事后精神上受到了巨大的打击,从而有意让读者感到迷惑。小说采取这一结构目的是让我们对受害者索尼埃产生同情;但另一方面,索菲对他的愤怒又不得不让人质疑他的诚实和正直。

科莱代表态度中立的观察者。他似乎没有什么秘而不宣的目的;与法希不同,他并不想借此案升官进爵。布朗仍未透露法希大力侦破此案是如科莱所料,想以此高调破案来巩固自身地位,还是他本人真的同天主事工会存在着某种关联。

第 21~25 章

综述:第 21 章

索菲回忆起祖父喜欢利用名画编制字谜。幼年时,祖父曾在闭馆之后带他参观过《蒙娜丽莎》。此刻,她对那幅画已经记得不大清楚。她意识到如果祖父想给她留口信,《蒙娜丽莎》是个好地方;而且他临死前一定去看过它。索菲决定返回电梯井,上楼去找那幅画。她让兰登独自去美国大使馆,并把自己的汽车钥匙交给了他。兰登边走边想索尼埃为何让索菲去找自

embassy without her and gives him the keys to her car. As he walks away, Langdon wonders why Saunière told Sophie to find him. Sophie could easily have figured out the puzzle in the message without him. While thinking about the letters "P. S." in the code, Langdon has a sudden realization. He starts running back to Sophie.

Summary: Chapter 22

At the Church of Saint-Suplice, Silas looks around the sanctuary and finds the Rose Line, a strip of brass on the north-south axis that is imbedded in the structure of the church. This line, a pagan sundial, was the zero longitude of the world before Greenwich, England, took that title. Silas has been told that the Priory keystone lies beneath the obelisk at the northern terminus of the line. He walks toward the obelisk. Meanwhile, Aringarosa arrives in Rome.

Summary: Chapter 23

Sophie tries to see whether her grandfather left her any messages in invisible ink by the *Mona Lisa*. Langdon reappears, out of breath. He asks Sophie if the initials P.S. mean anything to her aside from Princesse Sophie. She says that once, when she was younger, she saw a strange key in her grandfather's closet decorated with the initials P.S. and—as Langdon has already guessed—a fleur-de-lis. Saunière never explained what the key was for, but he said if she kept the secret, the key would one day be hers.

Langdon says that Saunière was a member of the Priory of Sion, an exclusive secret society involved in pagan goddess worship. The Priory has had many prominent members, among

己。没有他，索菲也能轻而易举地破译信息中的密语。想到密码中的“P.S.”，兰登脑中突然灵光一现，于是马上跑回去找索菲。

综述：第22章

巴黎圣叙尔皮斯教堂内，塞拉斯环顾圣殿四周，发现了玫瑰线——一条嵌入教堂地面、标示地球南北轴线的细黄铜线。它是异教徒使用的日晷，在伦敦格林威治夺走它的称号之前，曾是零经度线的所在地。塞拉斯曾被告知隐修会的楔石就藏在这条线北边终点的方尖碑之下，他一步步走向方尖碑。与此同时，阿林加洛沙也抵达了罗马。

综述：第23章

索菲正试图找出祖父是否在《蒙娜丽莎》旁边用显隐墨水给她留了什么消息，这时兰登气喘吁吁地跑了过来。他问索菲，对她而言“P.S.”除了索菲公主外还有没有其他含义。索菲回答说，她小时候曾经看到祖父壁橱里有把奇特的钥匙，上面装饰有“P.S.”字样的首写字母，兰登猜到钥匙上饰有一朵百合花。索尼埃从未解释这把钥匙是做什么的，但他说如果索菲能保守秘密，总有一天钥匙会属于她。

兰登说索尼埃是一个进行异教女神崇拜的高层秘密社团——郇山隐修会的成员。隐修会拥有包括

them Leonardo Da Vinci. It is known as the protector of a huge secret. Sophie thinks that this might explain the unthinkable scene she witnessed her grandfather taking part in. Meanwhile, Fache and his partners apprehend the truck and discover the bar of soap with the GPS tracker in it.

Summary: Chapter 24

Silas kneels at the base of the obelisk. Each of his victims told him that the keystone was hidden there. He knocks on the tiled floor and discovers that there is a hollow opening under the ground. He prepares to break the floor tile. Sister Sandrine, spying on him from the balcony, prepares to do her duty as a sentry for the Brothers of Sion. She thinks the stranger standing at the base of the obelisk is a message from the dead Brothers telling her that something is wrong.

Summary: Chapter 25

Fache calls the American Embassy and discovers that there was no message for Langdon. He backtracks through numbers on his cell phone and finds the number that Langdon called. When he realizes that it was Sophie Neveu's number, he becomes angry. He punches in the access code.

Analysis: Chapters 21–25

The police investigators, Sophie, and Langdon have all been in the same room with Da Vinci's *Mona Lisa* without realizing that the painting is central to discovering Saunière's secret. The *Mona Lisa* has historically been associated with secrecy; Mona Lisa's half-smile is famous for its ambiguity, and the sfumato style of painting, which produces a foggy ef-

达·芬奇在内的众多显赫成员，据说它保守着一个重大的秘密。索菲认为这或许可以解释她曾目睹到的祖父那不可思议的举动。此刻法希和同事拦住卡车，找到了那块埋有全球定位跟踪装置的肥皂。

综述:第 24 章

塞拉斯跪在方尖碑基座前，死在他手里的每个受害者都说楔石就藏在这里。他敲击地砖，发现在它下面有个空洞，于是就要击破地砖。在阳台上暗中监视塞拉斯的桑德琳嬷嬷也准备行使郇山兄弟会警卫的职责，她确定方尖碑基座旁站着的陌生人正是死难兄弟会成员警告她不对劲的那个人。

综述:第 25 章

法希给美国大使馆打电话，结果发现那里根本没有给兰登的留言。他回过头查看手机，找到兰登拨叫的号码，发觉竟然是索菲的电话，因此他恼怒万分，重拳打在存取方式按键上。

品评:第 21~25 章

警方调查人员、兰登、索菲与达·芬奇的《蒙娜丽莎》同处一室，却没人意识到这幅画是揭开索尼埃秘密的关键。《蒙娜丽莎》在历史上一直与秘密相关，她那似有若无的微笑因其难以捉摸而著称，达·芬奇作画时采用渲染技法形成了云遮雾绕般的效果，更增添

fect, increases the sense of mystery. Many have speculated about the cause of Mona Lisa's smile. Some, like the young Sophie, have failed to understand the painting's fascination. Like the meaning of the Mona Lisa's smile, the secret that Saunière knew seems to be hidden in plain sight.

Brown does not reveal the details of the terrible act Sophie witnessed her grandfather performing. At this point, it is impossible to know whether the act was as horrible as Sophie says, or whether there is some sort of Priory-related explanation for it. Brown has portrayed Sophie as a fairly open-minded person, which suggests that her interpretation of her grandfather's behavior is probably accurate.

Silas, like Fache, has failed to see that the women around him are not necessarily just unthinking, silent witnesses. Sandrine, like Sophie, has been able to use men's underestimation and her placement near the scene to exert influence on the action.

Modern communications present an interesting contrast to the ancient signs and symbols that preoccupy the book's characters. Fache's use of the cell phone as the way to break the code of Sophie's betrayal has more in common with modern-day spy movies than with the ancient mysteries that the rest of the novel explores.

Chapters 26–31

Summary: Chapter 26

Langdon believes that the *Mona Lisa* became famous because Da Vinci himself said it was his masterwork and took it with him everywhere he went. Langdon remembers teaching a

了它的神秘感。很多人都曾猜测过蒙娜丽莎微笑的缘由,而像年幼时的索菲一样,这些人并未发现它的魅力所在。索尼埃知道的秘密也如同蒙娜丽莎的微笑,隐藏在平淡无奇之中。

布朗没有透露索菲所目睹的祖父奇怪行为的细节,因此我们无从知晓它是否如索菲所说那样可怕,是否这即是与隐修会相关的某个仪式。索菲在布朗笔下是个思想相当开放的人,这就暗示了她对祖父行为的描述很可能是准确无误的。

塞拉斯和法希一样也将自己周围的女性视为多余且缺乏思考能力的无声目击者。而桑德琳与索菲也有共同之处,她也能利用男性对她的估计不足和自身地位对他们的行动施加影响。

现代化的通讯手段和主导书中人物的古代象征符号形成了有趣的对比。和书中探寻的古代神秘事物相比,法希利用手机侦破索菲的背叛行为和当代间谍电影有更多共同之处。

第 26~31 章

综述:第 26 章

兰登认为《蒙娜丽莎》之所以成为世界艺术名品,是因为达·芬奇宣称这是他的得意之作,而且无论到

class to a group of convicts as part of a Harvard program. He explained how the *Mona Lisa* embodies a balance between the feminine and the masculine. The name Mona Lisa, Langdon thinks, comes from the Egyptian god and goddess of fertility—Amon and L'isa. Some have speculated that the painting is a self-portrait of the artist in drag. This theory would confirm the painting's message of androgyny, the state of having characteristics of both sexes.

Back in the museum, Sophie and Langdon find blood on the floor and a message composed of six words scrawled on the protective glass over Mona Lisa's face.

Summary: Chapter 27

Fache tells Collet that Sophie helped Langdon escape from their grasp. Fache realizes that Sophie and Langdon must still be inside the Louvre and sends half of his men there. The other half he sends to "the only location in Paris where Robert Langdon could find safe harbor"—presumably the American Embassy.

Summary: Chapter 28

The message on the *Mona Lisa* is revealed: "SO DARK THE CON OF MAN." Langdon tells Sophie that the message refers to the Catholic Church's campaign to rid the world of female-worshipping religions and the Priory of Sion's opposition to this campaign. A police officer appears in the gallery and takes Langdon into his custody. Sophie hides behind the viewing bench.

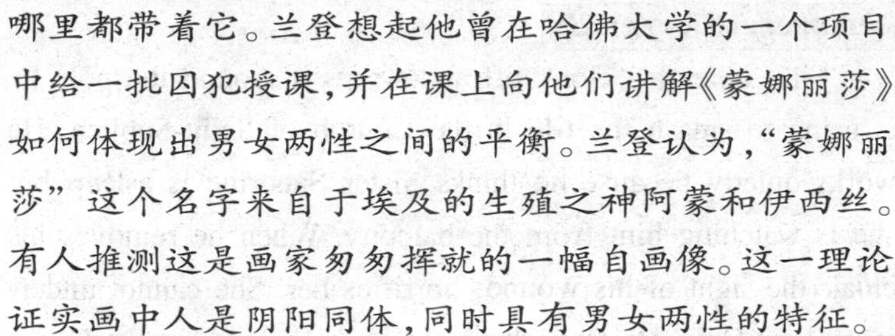
哪里都带着它。兰登想起他曾在哈佛大学的一个项目中给一批囚犯授课，并在课上向他们讲解《蒙娜丽莎》如何体现出男女两性之间的平衡。兰登认为，“蒙娜丽莎”这个名字来自于埃及的生殖之神阿蒙和伊西丝。有人推测这是画家匆匆挥就的一幅自画像。这一理论证实画中人是阴阳同体，同时具有男女两性的特征。

回到博物馆，索菲和兰登发现地板上有血迹，蒙娜丽莎脸部前方的防护玻璃上留下了一条由六个潦草的单词写成的留言。

综述：第 27 章

法希告诉科莱，索菲已经帮助兰登逃出了他们的监控。法希认为索菲和兰登一定还在卢浮宫内，于是他把一半警员派往那里，把另一半警员派到“兰登在巴黎唯一可能的安身之所”——美国大使馆。

综述：第 28 章

《蒙娜丽莎》上的留言是“男人的欺骗是多么黑暗”。兰登告诉索菲，这句话指的是由天主教会发动的、旨在清除女性崇拜宗教的运动，而郇山隐修会对这一运动持否定态度。一名警官出现在画廊并将兰登拘捕，索菲则藏到视线所及的一条长凳后面。

Summary: Chapter 29

Silas takes his cloak off and wraps it around the pole he is using to smash the tile in the Church of Saint-Suplice. He works quietly because he thinks Sister Sandrine is asleep, but she is watching him from the balcony. When he removes his cloak, the sight of his wounds horrifies her. She cannot understand how Opus Dei can observe such barbarous rituals. Under the tile, Silas finds a stone tablet with the reference number of a Bible verse from the book of Job. Excited, he looks through the Bible, but he finds that something is wrong. The verse reads: "HITHERTO SHALT THOU COME, BUT NO FURTHER." Sister Sandrine runs back to her room, where she retrieves four telephone numbers given to her for emergency situations.

Summary: Chapter 30

Claude Grouard is holding Langdon captive. Sophie comes out of the shadows and walks to *Madonna of the Rocks*, a painting on the other side of the chamber. She examines it with the UV light, but she sees nothing. Her grandfather often showed her this painting, so she is convinced there must be something in it. Moreover, the words he wrote on the *Mona Lisa*—"SO DARK THE CON OF MAN"—are an anagram for *Madonna of the Rocks*. When Sophie looks behind the painting, she finds the key decorated with the fleur-de-lis and the initials P.S. wedged into the frame. Thinking quickly, Sophie removes the painting from the wall and holds it hostage, forcing Grouard to put down his gun and release her and Langdon.

综述:第 29 章

圣叙尔皮斯教堂里,塞拉斯脱下披风,用它包住准备砸地砖的铁棒。由于以为桑德琳嬷嬷已经睡着,他悄悄地做着这一切,但嬷嬷此时正在唱诗班站台注视着他。塞拉斯脱去披风时,嬷嬷看到他身上的创伤,感到无比震惊。她无法理解天主事工怎么会遵循如此残忍的礼仪。塞拉斯在地砖下找到了一块石板,上面写有标示《圣经》中《约伯记》某一章节的数码。他激动万分,连忙去查询《圣经》,但却发现事情不妙,这一节中只写着:你将到此,但切莫前行。桑德琳嬷嬷跑回房间,找出四个发生紧急情况时拨打的电话号码。

综述:第 30 章

克罗德·格鲁阿德负责看押兰登。索菲走出阴影,来到房间另一头的《岩间圣母》画前。她用紫外线灯检查了一遍,却一无所获。祖父经常带她看这幅画,所以她猜测里面必有文章。此外,写在《蒙娜丽莎》上的字母"男人的欺骗是多么黑暗"颠倒组合之后,就是"岩间圣母"。索菲转到画背面,发现了一把刻有法国百合图案和首字母缩写 P.S.的钥匙。索菲当机立断,从墙上取下画,以此威胁格鲁阿德放下枪,让她和兰登逃走。

Summary: Chapter 31

Sister Sandrine calls the emergency phone numbers. The first three people she tries to get in touch with have just died. She is in the process of leaving a message on the fourth number's answering machine when Silas bursts into her chamber. He demands that she tell him where the keystone is. She does not know. Enraged, Silas bludgeons her to death with the candle stand.

Analysis: Chapters 26–31

In his interpretation of *Mona Lisa*, Langdon addresses the balance between the masculine and the feminine—a balance that is an integral part of the Priory of Sion's beliefs. Brown suggests that modern society, partly due to the Catholic Church's influence, has devalued women and banned them from positions of power, especially religious ones. Opus Dei is an extreme embodiment of these sexist principles.

Sister Sandrine is a casualty of the Church's campaign to oppress women. Like the witches, pagan priestesses, and midwives who were slaughtered by the Church during the crusades, she has been deemed disposable because of her sex. Silas's willingness to kill a nun who is fundamentally innocent of wrongdoing shows how fanatically convinced Opus Dei is of its own moral supremacy.

Brown suggests that religion is open to interpretation. For example, Silas likely believes that his faith, like that of the biblical Job, is being tested by God; for this reason, the delivery of the dead-end message to Silas in the book of Job is appropriate. Silas believes that the brotherhood's interpretation of scripture is a sacrilegious mockery. But the members of the

综述:第 31 章

桑德琳嬷嬷拨打了紧急电话号码,但是联系的前三个人都已经死了。正当她给第四个人留言时,塞拉斯闯了进来。他命令嬷嬷说出楔石藏在哪里,但她并不知道。塞拉斯怒火万丈,他用烛台连连抽打嬷嬷,直到把她打死。

品评:第 26~31 章

兰登通过解读《蒙娜丽莎》,强调男女两性的平衡是郇山隐修会信仰中不可或缺的一部分。布朗暗示,由于受到天主教会的部分影响,现代社会中人们依然贬低妇女,禁止她们登上权力位置,这在宗教领域尤为如此。天主事工会即是这类男性至上主义准则的极端表现。

桑德琳嬷嬷是教会压制女性运动的受害者。如同十字军运动中被屠杀的女巫、女性神职人员、助产士一样,因为是女人,她也被人视为用完即弃的物品。塞拉斯为了不法目的而杀死一个根本无辜的嬷嬷,说明天主事工会追求自身道德的优越已经达到了狂热的地步。

布朗认为宗教可以为人所解读。比如,塞拉斯相信自己的信仰与《圣经》中的约伯类似,都承受着上帝的考验,因此《约伯记》中那句告诉他已经走进死胡同的话送给塞拉斯的确是再合适不过了。在塞拉斯看来,兄弟会对《圣经》经文的理解冒犯了上帝,令人鄙

brotherhood surely feel that they have been truthful to the real religion and have observed it appropriately.

Chapter 27 is used largely to prolong the uncertainty over whether Langdon and Sophie will get out of the Louvre. This chapter is typical of the way Brown uses short chapters to build suspense. By cutting back and forth between different events that are occurring simultaneously, Brown creates a sense of immediacy and maintains excitement and suspense.

Chapters 32–37

Summary: Chapter 32

Sophie and Langdon run from the museum and get into Sophie's tiny car. They head for the embassy. Sophie wonders what the key opens. She thinks about the terrible thing she saw her grandfather doing. Ten years ago, she went to his chateau in Normandy and saw a large group of men and women in a secret room. A ceremony was going on and they were observing something (the reader is not told what). As she is remembering the bizarre and traumatic experience, Sophie stops paying attention the road. She hears sirens and sees that the police have blocked off the street leading to the embassy. When Sophie turns the car around, the police notice and follow her.

Summary: Chapter 33

Sophie and Langdon continue driving and try to formulate a plan of escape. Langdon looks at the key. Its handle forms a crucifix, a cross with four arms of equal length. Sophie has an idea and drives to the train station. Langdon is apprehensive

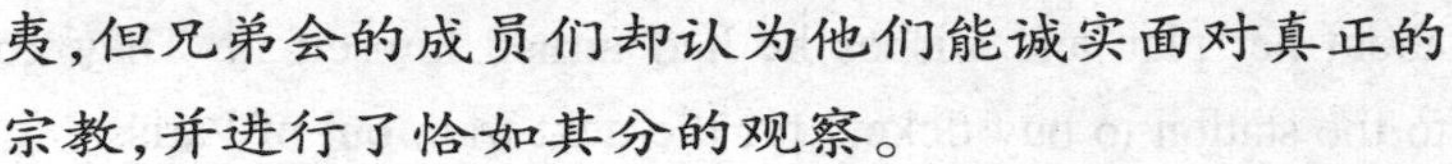
夷,但兄弟会的成员们却认为他们能诚实面对真正的宗教,并进行了恰如其分的观察。

第27章绝大部分都用来延长兰登和索菲能否从卢浮宫脱身的不确定性,这一章也是布朗利用短小章节营造悬念的典型事例。他在同时发生的不同事件间来回切换,使读者产生紧迫感,继续对故事兴味盎然,保持悬念。

第32~37章

综述:第32章

索菲和兰登跑出博物馆,开着她的微型汽车向大使馆驶去。索菲考虑着钥匙的用途,她回忆起10年前他看到祖父做的一件可怕的事。10年前,索菲来到祖父在诺曼底的别墅,她看到密室中的一群男女正在举行某种仪式并且观察着什么(作者在此并未提及是什么)。索菲只顾着回忆那次给自己带来重大打击的怪诞经历,而没有注意路面状况。她听到前面警报器鸣响,警方已经封锁了通向大使馆的道路。索菲掉转车头时被警察发现,他们一直在后面追踪。

综述:第33章

索菲和兰登一边继续向前行驶,一边琢磨逃生之计。兰登看着钥匙,钥匙柄被塑成了一个等边十字架的形状。索菲忽然有了主意,于是朝火车站方向驶去。

about her plan and wishes he had turned himself in. They go to the station to buy tickets for the next train out of Paris.

Summary: Chapter 34

At the airport in Rome, Bishop Aringarosa gets into the car that will take him to Castel Gandolfo, the Pope's summer residence. He remembers the last time he was at Gandolfo, at a meeting five months ago. On the ride that time, he was thinking about how the current Pope was too liberal, and how ridiculous it was that the Church used Castel Gandolfo, which houses an astronomical observatory, for scientific purposes. Religion and science cannot coexist, he believes. At the meeting, some terrible truth was unveiled. Now, as the Bishop travels to Gandolfo, he wishes the Teacher would call and say that Silas had the keystone.

Summary: Chapter 35

Sophie and Langdon buy two tickets and get in a waiting taxi. Langdon discovers an address written on the back of the key. They head toward that address.

Summary: Chapter 36

Fache tells Collet that the train tickets Sophie bought were probably decoys. He decides to alert Interpol to their flight.

Summary: Chapter 37

While the taxi drives through the Bois de Boulogne, a park full of sexual fetishists and prostitutes, Sophie asks Langdon to tell her about the Priory of Sion. He tells her the

兰登虽然明白她的计划,但他宁愿去投案自首。他们随后在火车站买了两张下一班离开巴黎的车票。

综述:第34章

罗马机场,阿林加洛沙主教上了汽车,他将前往教皇的夏宫——岗多菲堡。他想起上次来岗多菲堡开会是在5个月前。坐在车中,他考虑着现任教皇为何如此宽容大度,而教廷竟然将岗多菲堡设为天文观测台用于科学研究,这真是太荒谬了。在他眼中,宗教与科学不能共存。而在会上,一些恐怖的真相也显露出来。如今在前往岗多菲堡的路上,他希望导师能打电话告诉他塞拉斯已得到了楔石。

综述:第35章

索菲和兰登买好两张车票后就上了一辆等客的出租车。兰登发现钥匙背面有一个地址,他们径直朝那里驶去。

综述:第36章

法希告诉科莱,索菲买火车票可能是个诱饵,他决定向国际刑警组织发出警报追捕他们。

综述:第37章

出租车驶过布洛涅森林——一个挤满性恋物癖和妓女的公园,索菲请兰登谈谈郇山隐修会的情况。

brotherhood was established to guard a secret. Its legion of knights found a special cache of documents in a ruined temple. The cache made them rich and famous, but then a pope caused them all to be killed. Since then, the documents have made their way around the globe are now hidden in an unknown place. Langdon tells Sophie that the documents and the secret they corroborate are commonly known as the Holy Grail.

Analysis: Chapters 32–37

Brown draws out the revelation of the ceremony that Sophie witnessed, trying to sustain his readers' doubts about the fundamental goodness of the Priory of Sion. Everything else said about the organization, especially when contrasted with Opus Dei, makes its intentions seem honorable. But the fact that Sophie, a rational and educated person, could be so terrified and upset by what she witnessed suggests that perhaps not everything about the Priory is so upstanding.

Langdon can be timid. Despite increasing evidence that the police are not on his side, Langdon persists in wondering if he should have thrown himself on their mercy. His lack of intuition about the bad intentions of the police contrasts with his detailed knowledge of many other things in the world. He is a talented academic, but he lacks street smarts. Eventually, Langdon resigns himself to the chase and applies his intellect to uncovering the secret the Priory of Sion has been guarding.

Bishop Aringarosa is deeply conservative. He thinks the Church is now indulgent toward sin; he wants the Church to return to its punishment mode. He doesn't think the Church should conform to the cultural norms of the time, and he be-

兰登说人们建立兄弟会是为了保卫一个秘密。骑士团曾在一所废弃的寺院中找到了一批被藏匿起来的珍贵文件,这批文件使得他们钱财富足、声名卓著,但后来教皇却颁布命令将他们杀害。从那时起,这些文件便开始了环球之旅,如今被藏在一个不为人知的地方。这些文件和它们所证实的秘密就是众人皆知的圣杯。

品评:第32~37章

布朗对索菲目睹的仪式一直拖延不谈,使读者继续保持对郇山隐修会善良高贵本质的悬念。一切关于这一组织的叙述,特别是我们将它同天主事工会相对比时,都使它的宗旨看起来正直高尚。但事实上,像索菲这样理性而又受过教育的人都能被所见所闻吓得惊恐万状、心烦意乱,这就暗示了并非一切有关隐修会的事情都是正派无私的。

兰登可能是个胆小怯懦的人。即便有越来越多的证据说明警方不站在他这一边,兰登仍在考虑自己是否应该去投案自首,恳求警方宽大处理。对警方敌意缺少直觉和他具有的众多细致入微的知识形成了对比。兰登是位天才学者,但他缺乏对世态炎凉的理解。最终,兰登放弃了投案自首的想法,并把智慧投入到破解郇山隐修会守护的秘密当中。

阿林加洛沙主教极为保守,他认为教会正在纵容人们的罪孽,因而希望教会能恢复之前的惩罚方式。在他眼中,教会不应遵从当今的文化准则,而科学更

lieves that science is unnecessary. At the end of the chapter, when he pats his ring and thinks about how much power he will one day have, Aringarosa appears to be a tyrant-in-waiting, willing to ignore his own failings and shortcomings while judging others.

Fache's affection for technology, as detailed in previous chapters, seems likely to lead him astray. Within the constructs of the novel, Sophie and Langdon are not merely a female cryptologist and a schoolteacher, as Fache snidely calls them, but instead a team prepared to elude the technological dragnet that he Fache is setting out for them.

By bringing the Holy Grail into the novel, Brown taps a longstanding interest in the ancient holy secret. Some readers may associate the Grail with Indiana Jones or Monty Python, but even if they don't know anything about it beyond these vague associations, they are likely to be interested in the Priory's secret.

Chapters 38–44

Summary: Chapter 38

Langdon explains to Sophie that the documents the Priory protects are called the Sangreal, or Holy Grail. The Grail is not just a cup, as it is most commonly portrayed, but this group of documents. The cup, he explains, is an allegory for something. Langdon remembers showing his manuscript about the Holy Grail to his editor, who reacted dubiously to his theory. (Though Brown does not reveal what this theory is, he makes it clear that it is a controversial theory that does have supporters). Many prominent historians have written about this

是多余之物。本章结尾处,阿林加洛沙轻拍戒指,盘算自己有朝一日会拥有多大权力的形象,简直是个等鱼上钩的暴君,他在品评他人时绝不会想到自己有什么缺点错误。

从前面章节中的细节描述可以看出法希对技术的喜爱似乎已使他误入歧途。在小说的架构中,法希将索菲和兰登讥讽为密码破译员和教师,但他们绝不仅仅如此,相反他们组成团队,逃出了法希布下的技术罗网。

布朗将圣杯话题引入书中,激起了人们长期以来对古代神圣秘密的兴趣。一些读者可能会将圣杯与印第安纳·琼斯或者巨蟒组合加以联系,但即使对其中模糊的关联一无所知,他们也会对隐修会的秘密充满兴趣。

第38~44章

综述:第38章

兰登向索菲解释隐修会所保护的文件称为圣杯。圣杯并不像人们普遍描绘的那样是个杯子,而是一组文件。按照他的解释,圣杯是关于某事的一个寓言。兰登回想起自己将关于圣杯的手稿给编辑审阅时,他也是半信半疑(尽管布朗没有介绍这是怎样的理论,但他已表明这一理论虽有人支持,也会引起争议)。众多知名历史学家已对这一理论有所论述,但由于它不被《圣经》和教会支持,因此从未取得过合法地位。

theory, but it never gained legitimacy because it was not supported by the Bible or the Church.

Sophie realizes that their cabbie is about to turn them in. Holding him at gunpoint, she forces him out of his cab and makes Langdon take the wheel. Langdon can't drive a stick shift, but they manage to get away.

Summary: Chapter 39

Silas sits in the room at the Opus Dei safe house, fretting over the fact that even though he killed all of the brothers, he doesn't know where the secret is. He is also worried that by killing Sister Sandrine, he has put Bishop Aringarosa in danger. Silas considers killing himself. He feels he has let down the only man who has ever helped him. Silas remembers how the Bishop told him that Noah of the Ark was an albino, white like an angel. The Bishop said Silas, too, was destined for great things.

Summary: Chapter 40

Sophie takes the wheel, and they continue driving toward the address written on the key. As Langdon looks at the key, he thinks about the equal-armed cross engraved on it. The cross is very similar to the symbol used by the Knights Templar, the guardians of the Holy Grail. Nobody has seen the Grail since 1447, when a church fire forced the Priory of Sion to relocate it. Langdon is certain that when Leonardo presided over the Priory of Sion, he knew of the Grail's whereabouts. Langdon thinks the Grail probably hasn't been moved since then. Many historians study Leonardo's work closely in the hopes of discovering the secret of the Holy Grail's hiding

索菲发现出租车司机正打算把他们交给警方，于是她用枪逼司机下车，然后让兰登开车。虽然兰登根本不会操作变速杆，但他们还是成功逃脱了。

综述：第39章

塞拉斯坐在天主事工会的安全住房内，心情烦躁，他杀了兄弟会所有成员，却依然不知秘密所在。他同时也担心，由于杀了桑德琳嬷嬷，他已让阿林加洛沙主教身陷危境。塞拉斯想到了自杀，认为自己辜负了世上这唯一一个曾经帮助过他的人。他想起阿林加洛沙主教曾经告诉他，方舟中的诺亚就是一个像天使一样白的白化病人，而他——塞拉斯，命中注定要有一番作为。

综述：第40章

索菲换到驾驶位置，继续向钥匙上所标示的地址驶去。兰登看着钥匙，想到了上面雕刻的等边十字架和圣杯守护者——圣殿骑士所用的标志十分相像。1447年后再没有人见到过圣杯，一场教堂火灾迫使郇山隐修会将它再次转移。兰登可以确定，当达·芬奇执掌郇山隐修会时，他已经知道了圣杯的下落。兰登认为从那时起圣杯就没再被挪动过。许多历史学家都曾仔细研究达·芬奇的作品，希望能找到关于圣杯藏身之地的秘密。最近人们发现，达·芬奇的一幅名画——《受膜拜的麦琪》——曾在他死后为掩盖一条

place. It was recently discovered that one of Da Vinci's paintings, *Adoration of the Magi*, was painted over after his death in order to cover up a secret message. This discovery has fueled a lot of speculation about the conspiracy around the Grail.

Sophie wonders if the key is to the Grail itself, but Langdon thinks it unlikely that Sophie's grandfather was so high up in the hierarchy of the Priory of Sion that he had access such classified information. Sophie, remembering the traumatic event in which her grandfather participated, believes it is perfectly plausible that her grandfather had access to such information. They finally reach the address on the back of the key. It is the Depository Bank of Zurich, a Swiss bank.

Summary: Chapter 41

Bishop Aringarosa arrives at Castel Gandolfo, the Pope's summer residence, where he meets with the Secretariat Vaticana, the man in charge of Vatican City's legal matters, as well as with two high-ranking cardinals. They present Aringarosa with a suitcase filled with the Vatican bonds he requested. The Church officials are uncomfortable giving him such a large sum of money, which could easily be traced back to the Church. They don't know what the Pope will use the money for. Bishop Aringarosa signs an official document, which appears to be his resignation.

Summary: Chapter 42

In the Depository Bank of Zurich, Sophie and Langdon use the key to get through the elaborate security measures—gates, metal doors, and so on. They arrive at the front office, where a guard greets them and points them to an elevator,

秘密信息被重新描绘过。这一发现引起了人们对有关圣杯阴谋的众多猜测。

索菲怀疑这把钥匙是否就能通往圣杯，兰登认为这不太可能，因为索菲的祖父在郇山隐修会领导层中未必有如此高的地位，能够接触到这样的机密文件。索菲想起祖父给她造成心灵创伤的那件事，认为祖父完全能够获取此类信息。两人最终到达钥匙背面的地址——瑞士苏黎世储蓄银行。

综述：第 41 章

阿林加洛沙主教抵达教皇夏宫岗多菲堡，他在这儿见到了负责处理梵蒂冈法律事务的秘书及两位高级红衣主教。按他的要求，他们递给他一个装满梵蒂冈债券的手提箱。教廷官员对交给他如此大的一笔款项感到不安，因为人们很容易将此事追查到教廷这里，而且他们并不知道教皇将如何使用这笔钱。阿林加洛沙主教为此签署了一份书面文件，看上去就像是他的辞呈。

综述：第 42 章

在苏黎世储蓄银行，索菲和兰登用钥匙通过了大门、金属门等重重精工制作的安全措施。前门处的警卫向他们问好，并指引他们乘坐电梯前往金库。警卫

which will take them to their vault. The guard recognizes the pair from the news and calls Interpol and the bank's president, Monsieur Vernet. Sophie and Langdon make it to the vault only to find that they need an account number to access the box. They don't realize that they have been discovered—or that they are locked in the vault. Fache sends Collet to the bank to apprehend Langdon and Sophie.

Summary: Chapter 43

André Vernet, the bank's president, hurries to the bank after hearing that the police are after high profile clients. Part of Vernet's job is to keep the bank's name out of the press, and he hopes to diffuse the situation. When he enters the vault, he can't hide his surprise at seeing Sophie. He tells her that he was a good friend of her grandfather's. She shocks him with the news that her grandfather has been killed.

Sophie begs Vernet for the account number, but he refuses, saying that only the clients know their own account numbers. He promises to smuggle them past the police, but Sophie and Langdon do not want to leave until they have opened the safe deposit box. While Vernet goes up to the lobby to try turn the police away, Sophie and Langdon remain in the vault and try to figure out the account number. Langdon realizes that the number must be the string of digits Vernet wrote on the floor before he died.

Summary: Chapter 44

Langdon and Sophie have only one chance to enter the correct account number into the computer. Sophie looks over the numbers once more and decides that the account number

认出他们是新闻中通缉的人,于是拨打了国际刑警组织和银行行长韦尔内的电话。索菲和兰登成功进入金库,却发现只有知道账户名才能打开保险箱。他们并没意识到自己已经被人发现,或者换句话说,被锁在了金库里。法希派科莱去银行逮捕兰登和索菲。

综述:第 43 章

得知警方在追捕他的重要客户,银行行长安德烈·韦尔内急忙赶往银行。韦尔内的工作之一是使银行远离媒体,他希望能够平息此事。当他走进金库看到索菲时,他大吃一惊。他告诉索菲自己是他祖父的好友,但索菲的话让他更为震惊,索菲告诉他索尼埃已经被杀害了。

索菲恳求韦尔内告诉她银行账号,韦尔内断然拒绝,他表示只有客户本人才知道账号。他承诺会把他们从警察眼皮下面偷偷带出去,但索菲和兰登表示不打开安全保管箱他们是不会离开的。韦尔内走向大堂,试图把警察挡在门外,他们两个则留在金库内继续琢磨账号。兰登想到索尼埃临死前写在地板上的那行数字可能就是账号。

综述:第 44 章

兰登和索菲仅有一次机会在电脑中键入正确账号,索菲再次检查了这列数字,确定账号数字应该是

must be the Fibonacci sequence. The number works, and the electronic system retrieves a safety deposit box from the basement for them. Inside is a small, heavy rosewood box with a rose inlaid on the top: the Priory's symbol for the Holy Grail. Sophie and Langdon are surprised when they hear gurgling noises coming from inside the chest.

Analysis: Chapters 38–44

Though both Robert Langdon and Bishop Aringarosa are on a quest to find the Holy Grail, they are interested in it for different reasons. Brown dispenses hints that Langdon has had entanglements with the Church in the past, but Langdon's motivation seems to be essentially academic. In contrast, Aringarosa wants to find the Grail in order to cover up the truth and secure Opus Dei's power.

Silas's devotion to Bishop Aringarosa is extreme. He views the Bishop as his savior and finds his life's meaning in serving him and Opus Dei. His devotion is not only unhealthy, but dangerous. It returns him to the violent state of mind he was in before his conversion to Christianity. Silas's moral quandary over the killing of Sister Sandrine initially seems to be a sign that he has repented and realized how wrong he was to kill indiscriminately. But then it becomes clear that Silas is less upset about Sister Sandrine's death than about Bishop Aringarosa, whom he credits with his salvation. It seems that for Silas, anybody associated with Opus Dei is precious, and anybody outside of the fold is expendable.

Aringarosa feels contempt for Church officials not only because of their status as members of the new, more liberal church, but also because they are, in his opinion, weak men in-

斐波那契数列。数字输入正确，电子系统从地下室为他们传送上来一个安全保管箱。里面有一个沉重的玫瑰木的小箱子，箱顶上镶有郇山隐修会用来象征圣杯的玫瑰花。他们吃惊地听到箱中传来汩汩的流水声。

品评：第38~44章

尽管兰登和阿林加洛沙主教都踏上了寻找圣杯之旅，但两人的志趣截然不同。按布朗所设置的线索，兰登虽然过去曾和教会有过纠缠，但他始终是出于学术动机来进行探索。相比之下，阿林加洛沙寻找圣杯的目的却是掩盖真相和巩固天主事工会的力量。

塞拉斯对阿林加洛沙主教极为忠心，他将主教视为救星，并在侍奉主教和天主事工会中找到了生活的意义。他的忠诚不但有害身心，还会危及他人，这让他重新回到皈依天主之前的暴力状态。塞拉斯杀死桑德琳嬷嬷后面临的道德困境似乎提示读者，他已对自己不分好坏、滥杀无辜有所认识，并感到懊悔。但我们转瞬又明白，塞拉斯杀死桑德琳嬷嬷时的不安，远远不及他此时对于自己信任的救星阿林加洛沙的感情。对塞拉斯而言，任何与天主事工会相关的人的生命都价值千金，而这个圈子之外的人，都是可以牺牲的。

阿林加洛沙对教廷官员嗤之以鼻，不仅因为这些教会成员更为革新和宽容，而且在他看来这些人并不能拯救教会免于劫难。他之所以把他们拉进自己的计

capable of saving the church from catastrophe. He decides to implicate them in the plan himself because he is not sure that, given the choice, they would implicate themselves.

Brown again writes Sophie and Langdon, who are trapped in the Swiss bank, into a seemingly inescapable situation. By playing up the impressive trappings of the bank, Brown emphasizes the contrast between Sophie and Langdon's naiveté and the bank's sophistication. Brown wants to portray Sophie and Langdon as underdogs so that if they do prevail, their triumph will be that much more impressive.

André Vernet's appearance is something of a deus ex machina—a device from Greek plays in which a god suddenly descends from the sky and straightens everything out. Vernet is probably the only person who could have helped Sophie and Langdon get out of the bank vault without being arrested. Brown's reliance on characters like Vernet is convenient, but it might strike some readers as a bit of a cop-out, a too-handy device for a thriller writer who needs to get his characters out of a mess. More satisfying, perhaps, would be a scene in which Sophie and Langdon manage to extricate themselves without help.

Sophie's role as the intuitive member of the duo is emphasized again when she guesses her grandfather would have used a code number with meaning. At this point, Sophie is not only the person who uses common sense to get herself and Langdon out of scrapes; she is also the one who is better at interpreting human nature. Here, she takes on a more stereotypically female role, while Langdon plays the part of the non-intuitive, analytical male.

划，是因为他不能肯定，倘若给他们选择机会他们是否会投身其中。

布朗再次描绘了兰登和索菲两人，他们身陷瑞士银行——一个几乎无法摆脱的困境当中。布朗通过对银行机关的夸张叙述，加强了两人的天真与银行复杂装置的对比。他有意将两人写成失败者，这样如果他们能够逆中求胜便会更加令人印象深刻。

安德烈·韦尔内是一个扭转局势的角色。在古希腊戏剧中，天神会突然现身解决一切疑难问题，韦尔内的出场和这有点相像。他可能是唯一一个可以帮助兰登和索菲从银行金库脱身，而又不被警方逮捕的人物。布朗依靠韦尔内这样的角色固然写起来方便，但这也可能被一些读者看作惊悚小说家帮助书中人物脱离困境的方便道具；或许设置兰登和索菲凭自己的力量逃脱的场景会更令人满意。

索菲是二人组合中直觉较强的一方，这点在她猜出祖父利用密码传递信息时再次得到了印证。此时索菲不仅能利用常识使她与兰登脱离尴尬境地，而且她对人性的解读也更加出色。索菲在此扮演了一个较为模式化的女性形象，而兰登则是一个缺乏直觉、长于分析的男性角色。

Chapters 45–52

Summary: Chapter 45

Vernet puts Sophie and Langdon in the back of an armored truck, changes into a driver's uniform, and hides a gun under his clothes. As he drives them away from the bank, Officer Collet stops him and interrogates him. Vernet pretends to be a blue-collar driver and says he does not have the keys to the trunk. Collet sees Vernet's Rolex and grows suspicious, but ultimately he lets Vernet go.

Summary: Chapter 46

Silas is extremely upset that he has let down Bishop Aringarosa. He finally brings himself to call the Teacher, who tells him that Saunière left a message and that he should stand by for further instructions.

Summary: Chapter 47

Inside the box, Sophie and Langdon find a ball with letters written on each of its five panels. Sophie recognizes this as a cryptex, an invention of Leonardo Da Vinci's that provided a secure way to transport messages over long distances. A password is needed to get to the message inside the ball. Sophie and Langdon discuss the meaning of the rose that is on top of the box.

Summary: Chapter 48

Langdon realizes that they must be holding the Priory keystone. He says that only the leader of the Priory would have access to the keystone, and Sophie says she thinks her

第45~52章

综述:第45章

韦尔内将索菲和兰登两人藏在装甲卡车后车厢里,他换上了司机制服,又在衣服里藏了一把手枪。开车离开银行时,科莱将他拦住并进行询问。韦尔内假扮成司机,谎称自己没有卡车钥匙。科莱看到他的劳力士手表后起了疑心,但最终还是放行了。

综述:第46章

由于让阿林加洛沙主教失望,塞拉斯十分苦恼。但他最终还是鼓足勇气给导师打了电话,导师告诉他索尼埃留下了一条信息,他稍后会给他进一步指示。

综述:第47章

索菲和兰登在箱内找到了一个球状物体,上面的五个转盘上都写有字母。索菲认出这是达·芬奇发明的密码盒,可以用来安全地长距离传递信息,只要键入密码就能读到球状物里面的内容。索菲和兰登开始探讨箱顶上玫瑰的含义。

综述:第48章

兰登意识到他们手中的东西可能是郇山隐修会的楔石。他说只有隐修会的领导人才能拿到楔石,索

grandfather may have been the leader of the Priory. The car stops and Vernet lets them out, but then apologetically pulls a pistol on them.

Summary: Chapter 49

Vernet tells Langdon and Sophie to give him the box. He just heard over the radio that they are wanted for three other murders. Langdon realizes who the three must have been. He hands the box over to Vernet, but he also manages to put a spent shotgun shell into the mechanism of the door. When Vernet tries to shut them into the truck, the door balks. Langdon bursts out of the door, takes the box back, and gets back into the truck while Sophie drives away.

Summary: Chapter 50

Bishop Aringarosa, leaving Gandolfo, realizes that the Teacher might not have been able to reach him because his cell phone service was not strong in the mountains. He panics, worried that the Teacher will think something has gone wrong with the deal.

Summary: Chapter 51

Langdon proposes that he and Sophie visit his friend Sir Leigh Teabing in Versailles. Teabing is a religious historian and Grail scholar who might be able to help them. Langdon remembers a controversial BBC documentary about Teabing's Grail research. They head toward Teabing's estate, Chateau Villette.

菲认为祖父可能就是隐修会的领导人。汽车停下后韦尔内让两人出来,然后面带歉意地用手枪指着他们。

综述:第 49 章

韦尔内命令兰登和索菲交出箱子,他刚从收音机里得知他们还因另外三起命案被警方通缉。兰登马上明白了那三个人指的是谁。他一边把箱子递给韦尔内,一边设法把一粒子弹壳塞到门轴承上。当韦尔内想把他们锁在车内时,门弹开了。兰登趁机冲了出去,抢回箱子,然后和索菲开着车扬长而去。

综述:第 50 章

离开岗多菲堡后,阿林加洛沙想到山区手机信号微弱导师可能无法与他联络。他又惊又怕,担心导师可能会以为他办砸了事情。

综述:第 51 章

兰登建议索菲和他去拜访住在凡尔赛的朋友提彬,提彬是一位宗教史学家兼圣杯研究者,也许能帮上忙。兰登想起英国广播公司曾就提彬对圣杯的研究拍过一部引起争议的纪录片。他们动身前往提彬的庄园——维莱特城堡。

Summary: Chapter 52

At Teabing's estate, Sophie and Langdon reach Teabing on the intercom. He asks them three questions before letting them in.

Analysis: Chapters 45–52

The trope of an ordinary person transforming himself is common in thrillers. In order to feign innocence, Vernet flips between cultured and uncultured personas. He disguises himself as if he is used to it. In the course of *The Da Vinci Code*, many ordinary people break through their barriers to help the cause of the Priory.

However Opus Dei heard about Saunière's message (Fache is a natural suspect), the two factions in this novel are about to be drawn together. Until this point, the Silas story has functioned separately from the Sophie and Langdon story.

Sophie's memories of her childhood with her grandfather humanize Saunière and turn him into a major figure in the novel. Sophie's memories have also been instrumental in helping her figure out what her grandfather's final actions meant. The search for the Grail begins to seem like a treasure hunt just like the ones Sophie's grandfather set up for her when she was a young girl running around the house in search of her birthday present.

Langdon, the retiring academic, finally seems excited about the chase. When he realizes that Saunière was the head of the Brotherhood and that the other three members of the Brotherhood are gone, he understands that it is now his and Sophie's responsibility to figure out where the Sangreal, or the Holy Grail, is hidden, and to guard the secret. Now he seems

综述:第 52 章

在提彬的庄园,索菲、兰登通过对讲机联系提彬。提彬问了他们三个问题后把他们请了进去。

品评:第 45~52 章

在惊悚作品中,普通人改变身份角色屡见不鲜。为了假扮无辜,韦尔内在文明人和大老粗的两副面具间来回变换。他不断伪装自己,仿佛对此已习以为常。随着情节的发展,众多平常人为了隐修会的事业都做出了非常之举。

但当天主事工会得知索尼埃留下了信息时(法希是再自然不过的嫌疑人),书中的这两股派系也即将针锋相对。在此之前,有关塞拉斯的故事一直与索菲和兰登的故事分开叙述。

索菲有关童年时对索尼埃的记忆使得这一人物更加人性化,并成为书中一个重要角色。索菲的回忆也有助于她推断出祖父最后行动的含义。搜寻圣杯开始与她童年时的寻宝游戏有了共同之处,幼时她曾经在房前屋后跑上跑下寻找祖父送给她的生日礼物。

兰登,这个昔日的学者,也开始对这次追寻感到激动。当得知索尼埃是郇山隐修会的首领,而兄弟会的其他三名成员已被杀害时,他明白他和索菲有责任找出圣杯埋藏地点,并保守这一秘密。现在他似乎有了更强的责任感,更加投入地解决这个问题。正因他

to become more fully engaged with the problem and with his personal responsibility. Because he has become involved, he is inspired to take the kind of wily action—foiling Vernet and getting the box back—that until now has been the exclusive province of Sophie.

The Bishop's worries about cell phone service are slightly comical. He behaves like a nervous schoolboy waiting for a call from the girl he likes. But his nervousness also underlines the Teacher's power. The fact that the Teacher has secret knowledge gained by electronic eavesdropping does not provide any clues about his location, occupation, or allegiances. The only thing the reader really knows about the Teacher is that he is a mercenary.

For the first time in this part of the novel, Langdon thinks about Sophie in a sexual way. He smells her perfume as he leans over to speak into the intercom and thinks about "how close they are." Brown's interest in the romantic aspect of Langdon's and Sophie's relationship seems a little forced, however, almost as if he included it only in deference to the conventions of thriller novels.

Chapters 53–61

Summary: Chapter 53

Vernet calls the manager of the bank and has him activate the tracking system on the armored truck.

Summary: Chapter 54

Langdon smuggles the cryptex into Teabing's house and

已参与此事，这就激励他可以做出一些权变之举，比如说击败韦尔内夺回箱子。在此之前，这种举动一直都是索菲的专利。

阿林加洛沙对手机服务的担忧有些可笑，他的行为举止就好像一个紧张等待心仪的女孩给自己打电话的小男生一般。但是这种紧张也从侧面强调了导师的威慑力。导师通过电子窃听设备获取秘密信息的事实没有为他的所在地、职业或是拥护者们提供任何线索。读者唯一知晓的是这位导师是个唯利是图的人。

在本书这一部分，兰登首次以男性视角来看待索菲。侧身同对讲设备说话时，他嗅到了她香水的芬芳，不禁想到“我们竟是如此之近”。布朗对兰登与索菲的浪漫关系的描写似乎不太自然，但他不过是遵从了惊悚小说的惯例而已。

第 53~61 章

综述：第 53 章

韦尔内给银行经理打电话，要求他激活装甲卡车上装备的跟踪系统。

综述：第 54 章

兰登偷偷把密码盒带进提彬家，并把它藏在大起

hides it underneath a divan in the grand sitting room. Langdon and Sophie sit on the divan and Teabing enters the room. Langdon says that Sophie doesn't know the true story of the Grail, and Teabing says he will tell her.

Summary: Chapter 55

Teabing explains that Leonardo Da Vinci thought the New Testament was written by men, not God, and that some gospels had been left out. Constantine the Great was determined to unite his subjects under one religion, so he reformatted the Bible in 325 A.D. To make the idea of Jesus a unifying force for his subjects, Constantine turned Jesus from a leader into a holy man. Constantine also included in the Bible many symbols of the sun-worshipping religion his subjects had previously followed. Teabing shows Sophie a picture of the Da Vinci fresco *The Last Supper*. There is no chalice or Holy Grail present in the painting, as many people think, but only wine glasses for each person. Teabing says the Holy Grail is not a thing, but a person.

Summary: Chapter 56

Langdon explains that the Holy Grail is a woman. He shows Sophie the ancient symbol for male and female. The symbol for female resembles a chalice. The Holy Grail is just a metaphor for the embodiment of the sacred female, which has been lost through Christianity. Langdon and Teabing tell Sophie that the Holy Grail is not just any woman, but a specific woman. At this point the manservant, Rémy, sees photos of Sophie and Langdon on television.

居室的长沙发里。兰登和索菲坐在长沙发上,提彬进了屋。兰登说索菲并不知道有关圣杯的真实故事,提彬说他会给索菲讲解的。

综述:第 55 章

提彬解释道,列奥纳多·达·芬奇认为《新约》是由人编写,而非上帝所授,而有些福音书受到了排斥,只有很少几个被保存下来。康士坦丁大帝决心按自己的意志统一宗教,因此他在公元 325 年对《圣经》重新进行了修订。为使耶稣成为与之相关事物的统一力量,康士坦丁将耶稣从领导者改造成了圣人。此外,他还将自己先前信奉的日神崇拜宗教中的众多因素加进《圣经》当中。提彬给索菲看了一幅达·芬奇绘制的湿壁画《最后的晚餐》图片,和许多人想的不同,画上并未出现高脚酒杯或是圣餐杯,人们拿的不过是葡萄酒杯。提彬说圣杯不是一个物品,而是一个人。

综述:第 56 章

兰登将圣杯解释为一个女人。他向索菲展示了一些象征男女两性的古代符号,而象征女性的符号和高脚酒杯类似。圣杯其实是对在基督教流传当中所遗失的神圣女性的一种隐喻。兰登和提彬还告诉索菲,圣杯不是指任何女性,而是指一个特定的女人。这时提彬的男仆雷米在电视上看到了索菲和兰登的照片。

Summary: Chapter 57

Collet receives a tip about Langdon's and Sophie's location. He gets in his car and heads to Versailles. Meanwhile, Silas breaches the wall of the estate. He is determined to get the keystone.

Summary: Chapter 58

In Teabing's study, the scholars show Sophie a representation of Mary Magdalene in *The Last Supper*. In the painting, she is shown sitting next to Jesus. The painting also contains several representations of chalices and the letter M. Teabing says Jesus thought highly of Mary, to whom he was married. According to Teabing, Jesus gave Mary instructions to carry on his ministry. Peter the apostle hated Mary and was jealous of her. Mary herself was the descendent of the line of Benjamin, a powerful line. Jesus and Mary had a child, or children, they tell her.

Summary: Chapter 59

Bishop Aringarosa calls Opus Dei in New York to see if he has any messages and finds that a number was left for him. He dials it and reaches the French Judicial Police. A man comes on the line and says he has a lot to talk to the Bishop about.

Summary: Chapter 60

Teabing and Langdon show Sophie all of the books that substantiate their claims about the bloodline of Mary. Teabing says that the Holy Grail is a sarcophagus—Mary's body—and that the documents prove that everyone in Mary's blood line is

综述:第 57 章

科莱通过线报得知兰登和索菲的位置,于是开车前往凡尔赛。与此同时,塞拉斯破坏了庄园围墙,决心拿到楔石。

综述:第 58 章

在提彬的书房中,两位学者正向索菲说明达·芬奇如何将玛丽亚·抹大拉体现在《最后的晚餐》这幅画中。画中她坐在基督身边,此外还有数个对圣杯的反映,以及象征耶稣欣赏玛丽亚·抹大拉并已与她结婚的字母“M”。提彬认为,耶稣曾给玛丽亚·抹大拉指示让她继续统领信徒们,但门徒彼得对她又嫉又恨。玛丽亚本人是极具权势的本杰明家族的后裔,她和耶稣还有了孩子。

综述:第 59 章

阿林加洛沙给纽约天主事工会打电话,查看有没有给他的留言,结果发现有人曾给他打过电话。他拨打号码,接通的却是法国司法警察,电话另一头的一个男人说要和他好好谈谈。

综述:第 60 章

提彬和兰登向索菲展示了所有能够证实他们关于玛丽亚血统主张的书籍。提彬说圣杯就是盛殓玛丽亚遗体的大理石棺,这些文件可以证明每个与玛丽亚

related to Jesus. Teabing also says that the Merovingians, French royals, are also descendents of Christ, and that the founder of the Priory of Sion was a descendent. Sophie starts to think that perhaps her family has something to do with this. Then Teabing's manservant calls him into the kitchen.

Summary: Chapter 61

Langdon tells Sophie that neither Saunière nor her mother, whose maiden name was Chauvel, are Merovingian, so she could not be of the line of Mary. He tells her about all the modern mythology and works of art, from Mozart's opera *The Magic Flute* to Walt Disney's films that reference the story of the lost sacred feminine. Teabing comes back into the study and demands to know what is going on.

Analysis: Chapters 53–61

Brown begins to introduce more variables, perhaps because only a few secrets are left to uncover. Vernet, a man who initially seemed to be on the side of Sophie and Langdon, has now changed sides. It remains to be seen whether he knows something they do not and exactly why he betrayed them to the authorities.

Teabing says that he doesn't get letters from offended Christians, because smart Christians know that the Bible isn't all it seems to be. Brown glosses over the protests of the small faction of Christians who believe that the Bible was, as Teabing says, sent by fax from Heaven. By presenting the idea that most Christians are smart enough to realize that history has had an effect on the Bible, Brown asks his Christian readers to keep an open mind about what the characters in his

血脉相连的人均和耶稣有关。他认为梅罗文加王朝家族、法国王室以及郇山隐修会的创始人都是耶稣的后裔。索菲开始思考可能自己的家庭也和此事有关。随后提彬的男仆把提彬叫进了厨房。

综述:第 61 章

兰登告诉索菲,不论是她的祖母还是母亲,娘家的姓氏都是肖维尔,而不是梅罗文加,因而她不可能是玛丽亚的后代。接着兰登又向她讲述了从莫扎特的歌剧《魔笛》到迪斯尼的电影等现代神话和艺术作品,它们都涉及到了失落的神圣女性。提彬返回书房,要求他们说清事情的来龙去脉。

品评:第 53~61 章

大概是因为仅剩下少数几个秘密有待揭露,所以布朗开始在书中引入众多变数。韦尔内起初似乎是站在兰登一边,如今却改变了立场。对于他是否知道索菲和兰登不了解的一些事情,以及他为何叛索菲和兰登转投当局,这些都留待下文解答。

提彬说他从未收到过那些感到自己受了侮辱的基督徒的信件,因为聪敏的基督徒知道《圣经》不全是像它表面看起来的那样。布朗简要处理了小部分基督教徒的抗议,如提彬所说,这些人相信《圣经》是从天堂发出的传真。布朗通过提出一个观点,即多数基督徒都足够聪明、能够明白历史曾对《圣经》产生影响,从而请他的基督徒读者对他在书中所谈的人物保持

novel say.

Brown has already introduced the idea that the Holy Grail could be something other than a cup, but the idea that it could be a person, and a specific person at that, is new. Brown has thrown another theory in the mix and piques the reader's curiosity about what the Grail will look like when it finally materializes. The question is whether a single person has carried the secret all of these years.

Both Collet and Silas hope that if they find the keystone, the world will cheer them. Collet wants to impress Fache and redeem himself for his earlier missteps, and Silas wants to please the Bishop and the Teacher. Neither Collet nor Silas fully understand the historical significance of the object they seek.

Langdon refers to scotoma, which means the way in which the brain reinterprets the truth when it expects to see a certain thing. Scotoma gives *The Da Vinci Code* its power over our imaginations. Almost every claim made in the novel is the opposite of conventional wisdom. The idea that a woman sits by Jesus' side in *The Last Supper* is likely a new one to readers, as is the idea that Jesus had a wife and children. The fact that these theories are unfamiliar gives credence to Langdon's claim that the Church has hidden them.

Langdon's allusion to Walt Disney as one of the people who has promoted the Magdalene myth is unexpected, particularly because some feminist theorists have criticized Disney for propagating the myth of the helpless female. Langdon singles out *The Little Mermaid* as a film that contains Magdalene iconography. Perhaps, Langdon suggests, the helpless females of Disney have all referred to Mary, who was robbed of power by the Church.

开放宽容的心态。

布朗自己也曾提出过圣杯绝不仅是一个杯子,但关于圣杯是一个人、一个特定的人的看法却是个新鲜观点。布朗将其他理论与小说交融,从而使读者对圣杯具象化时的形象产生好奇。问题在于,如果这是单独的一个人,她能一直保守秘密吗?

科莱和塞拉斯都希望能找到楔石,那样的话全世界就会为他们欢呼喝彩。科莱是想让法希钦佩自己,以弥补先前的失误;塞拉斯则是为了取悦主教和导师。两人谁都没有完全理解他们搜寻物品的历史意义。

兰登谈到了盲点的概念;它指的是当大脑期望看到一定事物时,会对事实进行再次解读的方式。盲点赋予了《达·芬奇密码》超越想象的巨大威力,几乎书中的每个观点都和我们习以为常的知识格格不入。在《最后的晚餐》一画中,耶稣身边坐了一个女人以及耶稣也曾娶妻生子的说法,令读者感到新奇。由于我们并不熟悉以上理论,所以兰登关于教会隐匿真相的说法变得更为可信。

兰登暗示沃尔特·迪斯尼也是一个致力于宣扬抹大拉神话的人,这倒有点出人意料,因为一些主张男女平等的理论家们曾批评过迪斯尼,认为他所描述的都是些遭受迫害而无力反抗的神圣女性的故事。兰登指出电影《小美人鱼》中就包含了抹大拉的影子。也许他是在暗示我们,迪斯尼故事中所有无助的女性都象征了被教会力量驱逐的玛丽亚。

Chapters 62–67

Summary: Chapter 62

Teabing is about to throw Sophie and Langdon out, but when Sophie mentions that they have found the keystone, he lets them stay. Outside, Silas hears the word keystone and prepares to enter. He plans to make them reveal the keystone's location.

Langdon tells Teabing that all of the members of the Priory are dead. They guess that the Church itself figured out who the brothers were and killed them. They also surmise that the Church struck because it thought the Priory was planning to release the documents. Teabing says the Church may have thought the Priory would time the release of the documents to coincide with the end of the age of Pisces and the beginning of the age of Aquarius, when man will think for himself. Langdon tells Teabing where the keystone is. Silas enters the house with his gun drawn.

Summary: Chapter 63

Collet is outside the chateau. Fache tells him not to arrest the suspect without his presence. Collet thinks Fache is having doubts about Langdon's guilt, or that he wants to take credit for the arrest himself. Collet and his policemen find the armored truck in front of the house and Silas's rented Audi parked nearby.

Summary: Chapter 64

Teabing, Langdon, and Sophie look at the cryptex. Langdon tries to determine whether part of the box might contain a

第62~67章

综述:第62章

提彬正准备把索菲和兰登赶出去,但当索菲提到他们已经找到了楔石时,他又把他们留了下来。躲在门外的塞拉斯也听到了“楔石”这个词,他准备冲进去,逼他们说出它的下落。

兰登告诉提彬隐修会的所有成员都已经死了,他们推测一定是教会发现了他们的身份后将其杀害。据他们猜想,教会动手是因为他们觉得隐修会计划公布这些文件。在提彬看来,教会可能认为隐修会将选择在双鱼宫时代之末、宝瓶宫时代之初公布文件,而宝瓶宫时代被视为是人类可以独立思考的时代。兰登正要告诉提彬楔石的位置,塞拉斯拔枪闯进了房间。

综述:第63章

科莱呆在城堡外面,法希告诉科莱,在他到达之前不要逮捕疑犯。科莱认为法希对兰登是否有罪心存怀疑,或者他是想把逮捕疑犯的功劳据为己有。科莱和手下发现了房前停着的装甲卡车,以及旁边塞拉斯租来的奥迪车。

综述:第64章

提彬、索菲和兰登三人看着密码盒,兰登想找出箱子的哪个部分可以提供密码的线索。他在它的内部

clue about the password. He finds a small hole in the interior. When he pushes the end of a paper clip through it, the rose falls out of the wood. Behind the rose there are some lines of text. As he is looking at the text, Silas hits him on the head.

Summary: Chapter 65

Silas has Teabing and Sophie at gunpoint. He orders Teabing to hand him the cryptex. Teabing agrees and then slashes Silas with one of his crutches, right on the punishment belt strapped around Silas's thigh. Silas goes down, and they bind and gag him.

Summary: Chapter 66

Langdon, Teabing, and Sophie fool Collet and the police into going upstairs. Collet goes down to the barn and finds that most of the sports cars are there, with the exception of one.

Summary: Chapter 67

In a Range Rover driven by Rémy, the group drives across the fields and through the forest behind the chateau. Teabing has Silas at gunpoint in the back seat. Teabing makes a call and orders his plane prepared. He plans to take them to England, away from the French authorities. Silas refuses to give the group information about why Opus Dei wants to see the keystone. Langdon has an idea and asks to use Sophie's phone.

Analysis: Chapters 62–67

Brown hints that Collet, the good-hearted police inspec-

发现一个小孔，当从这个洞推动一个纸卷的末端时，玫瑰花从木头上掉了出来，玫瑰下方是几行文字。兰登阅读文字时，塞拉斯给了他当头一击。

综述：第 65 章

塞拉斯用枪威胁提彬和索菲，并命令提彬把密码筒递给他。提彬答应了，并趁机用拐杖痛击塞拉斯，正好打在他大腿上系苦修带的地方。塞拉斯倒在了地上，大家把他捆起来，并塞住了他的嘴巴。

综述：第 66 章

兰登、提彬和索菲把科莱和警察们骗上了楼。科莱来到马厩，发现除了一辆车不在，其他跑车都还停在那里。

综述：第 67 章

众人坐在雷米驾驶的陆虎车上，穿过田野树林，将城堡甩在身后。提彬在后座用枪指着塞拉斯，然后拨打电话指示私人飞机做好准备。他计划带大家飞往英国，远离法国当局。塞拉斯拒绝告诉他们天主事工会为何要拿到楔石。兰登突然想到了什么，于是借用索菲的电话。

品评：第 62~67 章

布朗暗示，好心肠的警探科莱可能在故事中扮演

tor, may yet have a key role to play in the story. Collet has a good feeling about Sophie and Langdon, and believes that Sophie would not be involved with Langdon if he were guilty. In some ways, Collet is the classic bumbling police inspector, but he also turns out to be a stand-in for the reader. He recognizes, as the reader does, the fundamental goodness of Sophie and Langdon.

Ironically, Silas is brought down by the punishment belt, the very object he thinks makes him more righteous and worthy than Sophie, Langdon, Teabing, and anybody else who is not in Opus Dei. But the pain that was supposed to elevate him has instead caused him to lose control of the cryptex.

This part of the novel is like the calm in the eye of the storm. Both Sophie and Langdon think relief is in sight. They believe they might be able to get out of France with the cryptex and figure out how to find the Grail without being pursued. They even permit themselves a moment of tenderness toward each other. Despite the possibility of escape, a sense of foreboding persists. Silas prays for a miracle to help him evade his captors, and the narrator says a miracle is indeed coming.

Chapters 68–75

Summary: Chapter 68

Langdon calls Jonas Faukman, his editor, who admits that he sent a copy of Langdon's recent manuscript to Saunière in order to get a blurb for the back of the novel from him. Teabing asks whether the novel was critical of the Priory, and Langdon says it takes a neutral stance. Teabing thinks the Pri-

了一个重要角色。他对索菲和兰登印象不错,认为如果兰登有罪索菲决不会参与此事。在某些方面,科莱是典型的笨拙警探,但有时候他也是读者们的替身。和读者一样,他也认识到了索菲与兰登的善良本质。

具有讽刺意味的是,令赛拉斯倒下的却是他引以为豪的苦修带。他自认为正是苦修带使他比索菲、兰登、提彬等天主事工会以外的任何人更加正直高尚、令人尊敬,但本应帮他提升境界的疼痛反而让他失去了密码盒。

小说这一部分犹如宁静的风暴之眼。索菲和兰登都觉得解脱就在眼前,他们相信可以带着密码盒离开法国,不被人跟踪,继续找寻圣杯,他们甚至彼此温柔相对了一会儿。尽管也许可以逃离此处,但不祥的预感仍然挥之不去。塞拉斯祈祷奇迹发生,帮他从俘虏自己的那些人手中逃出,而故事的讲述者则提示奇迹即将到来。

第68~75章

综述:第68章

兰登给他的编辑琼纳斯·福克曼打电话,福克曼承认他把兰登近来的一部手稿寄给了索尼埃,想让他为该书的封套写一段简短的评述性文字。提彬问这本小说是否批评了郇山隐修会,兰登回答说它采取了中

ory should have revealed where the documents were hidden. When they reach the airfield, the pilot does not want to transport Sophie and Langdon, but Teabing threatens him with the gun and offers him a bribe.

Summary: Chapter 69

In the jet, Teabing asks Sophie if she understands the gravity of her own position. If she can find the Holy Grail, Teabing says, she will have the power to reveal the great secret to the world. He wants to know what she plans to do with that power. Sophie says that when she finds the Grail, she will know what to do.

Summary: Chapter 70

At Chateau Villette, Fache is furious with Collet. André Vernet calls the police and tells them that contrary to what he said, Sophie and Langdon were at the bank that night. He says they took something from Saunière's account. At the same time, another agent has gone through Teabing's speed dial numbers and spoken with the airfield. He has discovered that Teabing spoke with them that night.

Summary: Chapter 71

On the plane, Langdon and Teabing try and fail to decipher the text on the back of the rose. Sophie takes the text from them and says it is simply written backwards, the way Da Vinci used to write in his notebooks. One can read it in a mirror.

立的立场。提彬认为郇山隐修会早就该公开那些文献的隐藏地点。他们来到机场时，飞行员不想带上索菲和兰登，但提彬用枪威胁他，然后又给了他些贿赂。

综述：第69章

在飞机上，提彬问索菲是否了解她自己身份的重要性。提彬说，如果她能找到圣杯，她就有权力向世界揭露这个伟大的秘密。他想知道她打算如何利用这种权力，索菲说找到圣杯后就知道该怎么做了。

综述：第70章

在维莱特庄园，法希对科莱发了火。安德烈·韦尔内给警察打电话并告诉他们他先前说的是谎话，索菲和兰登那晚就在他的银行。他说他们从索尼埃的账户上取走了一些东西。与此同时，另一位探员拨通了提彬的快捷号码，机场工作人员告诉他提彬当晚和他们联系过。

综述：第71章

在飞机上，兰登和提彬试图破译玫瑰装饰物背面的文字，但都失败了。索菲从他们那儿拿过盒子，她发现这段文字只不过是反方向书写的，达·芬奇的笔记就是用这种方式写成的，人们可以借助镜子进行阅读。

Summary: Chapter 72

Langdon, Sophie, and Teabing copy down the four-line poem inscribed in the box. It includes references to Mary Magdalene's family, the Knights Templar, and the Grail. It is written in iambic pentameter and in English, which the Brotherhood considered the only language uncorrupted by the church. The poem instructs them to find a headstone "praised by Templars" and then use another code, the Atbash Cipher, to decode the password. They feel a bit daunted about the prospect of tracking all this down.

Summary: Chapter 73

At the airfield, Fache cannot find out who is on Teabing's plane with him, but he does manage to determine where the plane will land. He tells his police to have the Kent local police, not the British intelligence service, to surround the plane.

Summary: Chapter 74

Langdon guesses that Sophie witnessed her grandfather participating in a sex ritual. Sophie confirms this. Langdon tells her it was the ancient ritual of Hieros Gamos. Before the Church controlled societal norms, he says, sex was viewed as a sacred union between male and female. Sophie tells him she saw men and women in the basement of her grandfather's house, where her grandfather was having sex with a woman.

Summary: Chapter 75

On his charter flight to Paris, Aringarosa speaks with Fache and is horrified to learn that the plan is collapsing so

综述:第72章

兰登、索菲和提彬抄下了刻在盒子上的四行诗。它提到了玛丽亚·抹大拉家族、圣殿骑士和圣杯。诗是五步抑扬格,用英语写成——英语被修士会视为唯一没有被教会污染的纯正语言。这首诗指引他们去寻找圣殿骑士赞扬的基石,而后用另一种编码——埃特巴什码——解开密码。对于追踪这一切的前景他们感到有些恐惧。

综述:第73章

在机场,法希没能查出飞机上和提彬在一起的人是谁,但他还是设法弄清了飞机的着陆地点。他告诉他的警员让肯特郡当地的警察而不是英国情报部包围那架飞机。

综述:第74章

兰登猜想索菲曾见到她祖父参加了一个性仪式。索菲证实了这件事。兰登告诉她那是古代的神婚仪式。他说,在教会控制社会规范之前,性被视为男性和女性间一种神圣的结合。索菲告诉他她曾看到一些男女在他祖父的地下室,而就在那儿他的祖父和一个女人发生了性关系。

综述:第75章

在飞往巴黎的包机上,阿林加洛沙和法希通了电话,并惊恐地得知计划颓败得如此迅速。他将全部的

quickly. He offers the pilot all of the Vatican bonds to go to London instead of Paris. The pilot asks for his ring instead. Aringarosa gives it to him, feeling sick.

Analysis: Chapters 68–75

Teabing thinks the Priory could be making a play for power, just as the Church is. Teabing's expression of his doubts is one of the only times the Priory is presented as anything other than a wholly positive group. Teabing's theory is an interesting one and, if true, would make the last third of the novel much more complex. It is hard, however, to imagine the kindly Saunière involved in anything bad.

Sophie is now filling the familiar thriller role of the ordinary person put in a position of great importance. This typical, almost stereotypical, construction allows the reader to imagine herself as the protagonist. Readers can imagine that, given the chance, they would show the same kind of resolve and strength that Sophie does.

The mystery of Vernet's continued treachery continues to puzzle. It isn't clear why Vernet would decide to help Sophie and Langdon and then suddenly change his mind and stop helping them. Vernet is one of the only characters whose motivations haven't been closely examined. His sudden decision to tell the truth about what happened at the bank is highly suspect. Perhaps Opus Dei has gotten to him.

Once again, Saunière has hidden a message in a very simple way. Like the anagrams of famous paintings, the mirror writing is a level of code that even the very young can understand and decipher. Although this simple cryptography allows Sophie to again show up the men, it seems a bit unbelievable

梵蒂冈债券给了飞行员，要求飞往伦敦而不是巴黎。但那个飞行员却想要他的戒指，阿林加洛沙只好把戒指给了他，内心感到十分难受。

品评:第 68~75 章

提彬认为就像教会那样，郇山隐修会可能在玩弄权术。提彬所表达的这些疑惑是郇山隐修会唯一一次没有被视为一个完全正面的组织。他的理论很有趣，如果正确，会使小说余下的 1/3 更为错综复杂。然而，我们很难想象和善的索尼埃会牵涉进什么不好的事中。

索菲现在正填补了人们熟悉的惊悚故事中处于十分重要位置的普通人的角色。这种典型的、近乎程式化的塑造使读者能够把她想象成小说中的主角。读者甚至会想，如果有那样的机会，他们也会表现出和索菲一样的决心和力量。

韦尔内连续背叛的谜团仍然不得其解。为什么韦尔内先是决定帮助索菲和兰登，而后又突然改变主意不再帮助他们，这点目前还不清楚。韦尔内是唯一一个个人动机还未被进一步察觉的人。他突然决定说出银行发生的真相的举动十分可疑，有可能是受了天主事工会的影响。

索尼埃又一次以十分简单的方式隐藏了信息。像著名的油画中颠倒字母顺序构成的片语一样，反写是一种即使是孩子也能读懂的密码。虽然这种简单的密码术让索菲又一次胜过了两位男士，但如此重要的秘

that such an important secret would be hidden almost in plain sight. On the other hand, the mirror writing reinforces Langdon's theory that the most important answers are always self-evident.

Brown attempts to shock his readers out of their usual assumptions by describing iambic pentameter as the meter scheme of the divine feminine. Most people probably learn about iambic pentameter in English class and never think about any relationship to gender. Brown wants the process of reading this novel to be a discovery, a series of new understandings about things that seem like unremarkable fixtures in the cultural landscape. In the same way Brown challenges the reader's way of thinking about iambic pentameter and the *Little Mermaid*, he also challenges assumptions about sex, suggesting it is a divine act that has been demonized by the church.

Brown has yet to reveal the full extent of the plan to which Aringarosa refers. It must be a crucial endgame if Aringarosa is willing to sacrifice his diamond ring for it. Aringarosa is extremely materialistic, and the pilot's comment—"What kind of priest carries that much money around with him?"—reveals how far Aringarosa has fallen from priestly ideals.

Chapters 76–82

Summary: Chapter 76

Langdon has a realization about the "headstone praised by Templars" which appears in the poem. The Knights Templar were accused of devil worship during the time of Pope

密竟会隐藏的如此明显，这似乎有些令人难以置信。另一方面，这种反写也强调了兰登的理论，即最重要的答案总是不证自明的。

布朗把五步抑扬格描绘成代表神圣女性的格律，试图以这种超越读者一般假想的方式达到震撼的效果。许多人可能都在英语课上学习过五步抑扬格，但从没想到它与性别有什么联系。布朗希望人们把读这本小说的过程当作一种发现，从而对那些在文化景观中看似平常的固定概念产生一系列新的理解。同样，布朗不仅对抗了读者对五步抑扬格和《小美人鱼》的思考方式，他还对性观念提出了挑战，认为性是一种神圣的行为，后来却被教会妖魔化了。

布朗还不得不揭露出阿林加洛沙所指的全部计划。如果阿林加洛沙为了它情愿牺牲他的戒指，那么这一定是一场终极较量。阿林加洛沙十分崇尚物质，飞行员的话——“什么样的牧师能随身带着那么多钱？”——则显示出阿林加洛沙这一人物已经不再是理想的神父形象。

第76~82章

综述：第76章

兰登对那首诗中出现的“圣殿骑士赞美的基石”有了领悟。在克雷芒教皇时代，圣殿骑士曾因异教崇

Clement. The god they purportedly worshipped sometimes appeared as a large stone head, the head of Baphomet. Langdon and Teabing agree that this must be the password for the cryptex.

Summary: Chapter 77

Langdon, Sophie, and Teabing use the Atbash Cipher to decode the word Baphomet. The word they unearth is Sofia, the Greek word for wisdom and a variation of Sophie's name.

Summary: Chapter 78

When Sophie opens the cryptex, she finds another cryptex wrapped in a piece of vellum with a poem written on it. The poem includes a reference to a knight who is buried in London. Teabing says he knows where they should look.

Summary: Chapter 79

Collet, still at the chateau, is supervising the team that is looking for evidence there. One of the examiners has found a postcard of a cathedral with Teabing's ideas about how the architecture resembles a vagina, as well as Teabing's list of speculations as to who has been the head of the Priory over the years.

Summary: Chapter 80

Teabing tells Sophie and Langdon that he plans to bribe officials to let them into England without passports. Langdon is skeptical, but Teabing convinces him that his status as an eccentric old knight will help him get away with it. The pilot says the control tower has asked him to land in a different

拜而受到指控。据说他们崇拜的神有时呈现为一个巨大的头部石像,即鲍芙默神的头。兰登和提彬一致认为这一定是密码盒的密码。

综述:第 77 章

兰登、索菲和提彬用埃特巴什码来破解鲍芙默这个词。他们挖掘出的词是 Sofia, 在希腊语中代表智慧,也是索菲名字(Sophia)的一种变形。

综述:第 78 章

当索菲打开密码盒时,她发现里面是另一个用羊皮纸裹着的密码盒,羊皮纸上还写有一首诗。诗中提到一个被埋在伦敦的骑士。提彬说他知道他们该去哪寻找。

综述:第 79 章

科莱还在庄园里,他指挥一队人马在那儿寻找证据。其中一个检察官发现了一张印有大教堂的明信片, 上面还有提彬关于这个建筑如何与阴道形似,以及提彬推测出的郇山隐修会历届长老的名单。

综述:第 80 章

提彬告诉索菲和兰登他打算贿赂官员,让他们不用护照就能进入伦敦。兰登有些怀疑,但提彬让他相信,他作为一位古怪的老爵士的身份能够帮兰登逃脱处罚。飞行员说控制塔要他在另一个地方降落,并且

place and to keep everybody on the plane. Thinking this sounds suspicious, Teabing goes to the front of the plane to try to bribe the pilot.

Summary: Chapter 81

Simon Edwards, the manager of Biggin Hill Airport, watches Teabing's plane taxi onto the runway. Unexpectedly, the plane heads toward Teabing's private hangar, which was not part of the plan. Before the police arrive at the hangar, Langdon and Sophie exit the plane and drag Silas into the limousine. When the police arrive and search the cabin, they find nobody.

Summary: Chapter 82

Teabing explains that the knight a Pope interred was a Knight Templar, or one of the knights of the Priory, and that he was interred at the Temple Church in London. If they can find that tomb, they will find a clue about the "missing orb" that was supposed to be buried with this knight. While Teabing discusses directions with Rémy, Sophie and Langdon talk about whether the truth about the Magdalene should be revealed to the world. Langdon says it might be better to let people believe the myths that help them have faith. Sophie isn't sure she agrees.

Analysis: Chapters 76–82

Brown implies that Langdon's revelations are now inspired by intuition, not logical thinking. It is while he is being rocked in the plane to the rhythm of iambic pentameter and the imagined sounds of the sex ritual that Langdon comes to a

要每个人都呆在飞机上。提彬觉得这些话有些可疑，便来到飞机的前舱试图贿赂飞行员。

综述：第81章

比金山机场的一位长官西蒙·爱德华兹看到提彬的私人飞机在跑道上。出乎意料的是，飞机驶入了提彬的私人飞机库，这并不在计划之内。在警察到来之前，兰登和索菲下了飞机并拉着塞拉斯躲进了豪华轿车。警察到达后搜查了机舱，但没有发现任何人。

综述：第82章

提彬解释说教皇埋葬的骑士是一个圣殿骑士，或者是郇山隐修会的一名骑士，他就被埋葬在伦敦的圣殿教堂。如果他们能找到那个坟墓，他们就能找到关于那个本该和骑士埋在一起的“遗失的圆球”的线索。提彬和雷米讨论方向时，索菲和兰登谈到是否应该将抹大拉的秘密公布于众。兰登说也许让人们相信那种有助他们树立信仰的神话会更好。索菲并不确定她是否同意这种观点。

品评：第76~82章

布朗暗示现在兰登获得的启示是由直觉激发的，而并不是出于逻辑思维。当他在飞机上颠簸时，五步抑扬格的韵律和想象中性仪式上的声音使兰登得到

realization about the headstone. It almost sounds as if he is channeling the knowledge necessary to unlock the mystery. In the plane, Langdon relies on a stereotypically female trait—intuitiveness—to decipher a problem.

Teabing refers to Saunière as a "pitiless architect." Indeed, Saunière left an amazing number of clues to be solved. The question is whether Saunière set up so many steps in order to keep the Grail's secret, or whether he was being excessive.

Collet's and the examiner's total lack of knowledge about the study of the divine feminine makes them uncomfortable with Teabing's ideas about the shape of the cathedral nave. They are typical of close-minded people who take offense at the unorthodox ideas espoused by Teabing and his fellow religious scholars. Ironically, close-mindedness probably saves Teabing and his fellow fugitives from falling under even more suspicion. Most people consider their ideas simply eccentric and bizarre—not dangerous.

Teabing is convinced that he can operate outside of the law because of his tremendous wealth and status as a knight. So far, he has managed to do exactly as he pleases, escaping tricky situations with bribes and sly moves.

This chapter follows traditional thriller conventions: Sophie and Langdon get off the plane unseen, and the group prepares a sleight of hand to escape an inescapable situation. The narrator first presents the situation from the point of view of Simon Edwards and the police: Teabing exits the plane, and the police search the cabin and find nothing. Bewildered, they let Teabing go. At the end of the chapter, the narrator doubles back and explains how the other three got into the limousine. This method of narrative stretches each puzzle over the length

了有关基石的启示。这听上去似乎是他正把必要的知识引向谜团的破解。在飞机上，兰登依靠着典型的女性特质——直觉——破解了问题。

提彬把索尼埃视为“无情的设计者”。索尼埃的确留下了大量亟待破解的线索。问题在于索尼埃是否会为保守圣杯的秘密而设下了如此多的步骤，或者他这样做是否有些过度。

科莱和检察官十分缺乏对神圣女性研究的知识，这使得他们对提彬有关大教堂中部形状的见解感到不适。他们是一群典型的思想狭隘的人，他们强烈反对提彬和他那些研究宗教的学者朋友所拥护的挑战传统的思想。具有讽刺的是，思维狭隘却能帮助提彬和他逃亡的伙伴免于陷入更多的嫌疑，因为大多数人都认为他们的观点仅仅是古怪、离奇，但并不危险。

提彬让人相信，他巨大的财富和爵士的身份能让他不受法律制约。到目前为止，他都是按照他高兴的方式行事，通过贿赂和狡诈的行为他成功地逃脱了棘手的环境。

本章遵循了传统惊悚小说的习惯：索菲与兰登在未被发觉的情况下下了飞机，这群人设计了一个巧妙的方法逃离了本不可逃脱的境况。叙述者首先从西蒙·爱德华兹和警方的视角呈现了这一情况：提彬走出飞机，接着警察搜查了机舱但却没有发现任何人。惊慌失措之下，他们放走了提彬。在本章结尾，叙述者再次回溯解释了这三个人是如何溜进那辆豪华汽车

of the chapter, giving us a chance to guess what the solution might be.

Again in this chapter, Brown addresses the importance of knowledge. If faith is based on myths, Langdon suggests, then people with knowledge should leave those myths alone in order to preserve faith. In the context of the rest of the novel, which has suggested that the cover-up of this great secret has caused pain to many people, Langdon's suggestion seems to ignore the moral implications of keeping this particular secret.

Chapters 83–88

Summary: Chapter 83

Teabing lies his way into the Temple Church. He tells Sophie and Langdon that the Knights Templar used to run a primitive sort of bank, storing gold in their churches and allowing people with the right documents to withdraw the gold while they were traveling. Teabing, Sophie, and Langdon make their way into the tomb, where ten knights lie.

Summary: Chapter 84

Outside of the Temple Church, Rémy drinks vodka and thinks about how he will soon be rich. He unties Silas and tells him that he, too, serves the Teacher. They each take a gun and Rémy says they have a job to do. At the airfield, Fache is furious with the policemen who have not stopped Teabing.

Summary: Chapter 85

Teabing, Sophie, and Langdon try and fail to find the

的。这种叙述方法把每个谜题拉伸到了覆盖整章的长度，给我们提供机会去猜想可能的解决方案。

布朗又一次在本章中强调了知识的重要性。如果信仰像兰登认为的那样，是以神话为基础的，那么具有知识的人应该为了坚守信仰而把神话置之一边。小说余下的部分向我们展示了揭露这个巨大的秘密将会给许多人造成痛苦，而兰登的建议似乎忽视了保守这个特殊秘密的道德意义。

第83~88章

综述：第83章

提彬借故进入了圣殿教堂。他告诉索菲和兰登，圣殿骑士曾设立了一个原始形式的银行，他们将黄金存在教堂里，并且在旅行时凭有效证明支取。提彬、索菲和兰登来到了安放着十骑士的墓室。

综述：第84章

圣殿教堂外，雷米喝着伏特加，心里想着自己很快就会成为有钱人了。他给塞拉斯松了绑，告诉他自己也为导师效力。他们每人拿上了一把枪，雷米说有件事要他们去做。在飞机场，法希因为警员们未能阻止提彬而大发雷霆。

综述：第85章

提彬、索菲和兰登试图寻找诗中提到的失踪的圆

missing orb to which the verse referred. There are ten tombs containing knights; nine of the tombs are decorated with statues of knights. One has no statue.

The altar boy who let them in comes back and asks them questions. He hears a sound and goes to investigate. Rémy and Silas, who have entered, threaten him. The boy wets his pants in fear, and then he is allowed to run away.

Summary: Chapter 86

Silas holds Langdon at gunpoint and demands the cryptex, but Langdon threatens to smash it on the floor and ruin the papyrus inside unless Silas lets Sophie and Teabing go. Since the Teacher has had Rémy instruct Silas not to shoot anyone, Silas doesn't know what to do. The Teacher has also told Rémy not to show his face, but Rémy takes Teabing at gunpoint and makes Langdon give Silas the cryptex. Rémy leaves with Teabing. Silas keeps Langdon and Sophie at gunpoint.

Summary: Chapter 87

At the Chateau, one of the agents comes in from the barn and tells Collet to come look at something. In a loft in the barn, out of view, a high-tech surveillance station is set up. Collet asks who is being observed, and the agent says the answer will surprise him.

Summary: Chapter 88

Sophie and Langdon descend into the subway. Sophie tells Langdon that the best thing they can do for Teabing is to call the police on Rémy and Silas and turn them into fugitives.

球,但一无所获。那里共有十间安放着骑士的墓室,其中九间都装饰有骑士的雕像,只有一间没有。

放他们进来的祭台助手回来问了他们几个问题。他听到了声响,于是前去察看。雷米和塞拉斯进入了墓室,他们威胁祭台助手。由于极度惊恐,他尿湿了裤子,之后他们把他放走了。

综述:第86章

塞拉斯用枪指着兰登逼他交出密码盒,但兰登威胁说除非放索菲和提彬离开,否则他就摔碎密码盒,毁掉里面的莎草纸。由于导师通过雷米告诫过塞拉斯不可以向任何人开枪,此时塞拉斯不知道该如何是好。导师还曾命令雷米不要露面,但雷米还是用枪对准了提彬,他让兰登将密码盒交给塞拉斯。雷米带着提彬离开了,塞拉斯则继续用枪指着兰登和索菲。

综述:第87章

在庄园里,一名特工进来叫科莱到谷仓里看些东西。在谷仓阁楼里一个看不到的地方,建有一个高科技的监听台。科莱询问监听的是谁,特工说答案一定会让他大吃一惊。

综述:第88章

索菲和兰登进入地铁站。索菲告诉兰登解救提彬的最好办法就是报警,把雷米和塞拉斯作为逃犯来追

Langdon wants to go to a library and look up one of the phrases from the poem on an electronic database. But when Sophie calls the police, they transfer her to Fache, who tells her he knows Langdon is innocent and he wants her to come into the London police station to ensure her own safety.

Analysis: Chapters 83–88

The difference between the Anglican Church and the Catholic Church of Rome, while not explicitly analyzed, is significant to the story. Teabing refers to the Church of England, or the Anglican Church, and its propensity for bleak architecture. Anglicans and other non-Catholic sects of Christianity differentiated themselves from Roman Catholics through lack of decoration and artifice. The Roman Catholic affection for theater, which we have seen embodied by Aringarosa and his enormous ring, was offensive to some Christians, who split off to form their own sects. The Knights Templar's association with this bleak and unadorned place, then, is appropriate.

Rémy is revealed as a traitor when he fails to come to Teabing's aid during Silas's attack. Still, it comes as a shock to find that he is betraying his employer simply for money. Rémy does not want to be a servant to Teabing for his entire life, so he turns against the employer who has been so kind to him. Rémy's betrayal echoes the biblical story of Judas, who betrayed Jesus for money.

The tombs are a classic dead end of the type Brown seems to favor. Teabing and Langdon do not know it, but the tombs do not actually contain bodies. They are just statues placed over empty space.

In this part of the novel, Brown gets closer to revealing

捕。兰登想去图书馆用电子数据库查询诗中的一个词。当索菲打电话给警局时,他们将电话转给了法希,法希告诉索菲他知道兰登是无辜的,并希望她去伦敦警察局以确保她的安全。

品评:第83~88章

尽管并未明确指出,但英国国教教会与罗马天主教会的分歧在本故事中起了重要作用。提彬提到了英国国教,或英国圣公会,以及它简朴的建筑风格。圣公会以及其他非天主教的基督教教派与罗马天主教的分歧主要体现在其对于奢繁装饰的精简上。罗马天主教对于大礼堂的热衷在阿林加洛沙和他硕大的指环上可见一斑,一些基督徒对此相当反感,于是他们脱离了天主教,建立了自己的教派。因此,圣殿骑士选择这个荒凉、朴素的场所是再合适不过了。

在提彬被塞拉斯攻击时, 雷米没有上前帮助提彬,从而表明他是一个叛徒。他仅仅为了钱就背叛了他的主人,这点让人相当吃惊。提彬一直对他很好,可不想一辈子只做仆人的雷米还是背叛了他的主人。雷米的背叛影射了《圣经》中犹大为了金钱而背叛耶稣的故事。

坟墓似乎是布朗一贯钟爱的典型的终结方式。提彬和兰登不知道坟墓中实际上并没有尸体,只是在空旷的空间里安放着几尊雕像。

从小说的这一部分可以看出,导师不希望在执行

the identity of the Teacher when he reveals that the Teacher doesn't want anyone to get hurt in the process of carrying out this mission. This revelation about his personality, combined with the fact that he has access to electronic surveillance and that he is not known to Bishop Aringarosa, suggests that perhaps he is not associated with the Church. At this point, the identity of the Teacher is the second most important secret of the book, after the location of the Grail itself.

In the subway, Sophie and Langdon reverse roles: for once, Sophie is the one who wants to involve the authorities, and Langdon is the one who is leery of the police. Since they found Saunière, Langdon has dropped his naiveté and become suspicious and cautious. In one way, *The Da Vinci Code* is not just a thriller but also a coming-of-age tale about Langdon.

Chapters 89–95

Summary: Chapter 89

Fache is in Teabing's plane with the box, which he found in the safe. He sees that the cryptex is empty. He takes a call from Vernet, who is desperate to get the box back and save his bank's reputation.

Summary: Chapter 90

At the chateau, Collet discovers that the computer in the barn was conducting surveillance on five separate people, including Jacques Saunière. The other four people are important figures, including the head of French Intelligence. The agents on the scene also find blueprints that show that the bug was hidden in the replica of a knight on Saunière's desk.

任务时有人受到伤害,布朗由此更进一步揭露了导师的身份。透过他的这一性格特点,以及他可以使用电子监控器和阿林加洛沙主教并不认识他的事实,都暗示了或许他与教会并没有关系。目前,导师的身份是仅次于圣杯所在地的第二大秘密。

在地铁里,索菲与兰登的角色发生了转换:只有这一次,索菲希望权力机构的介入;而兰登则对警方怀有戒心。自从他们发现了索尼埃,兰登就不再轻信他人,他变得心有疑虑且小心谨慎。从某种意义上说,《达·芬奇密码》不只是一部惊悚小说,它也是一个关于兰登逐渐走向成熟的故事。

第89~95章

综述:第89章

法希坐在提彬的飞机上,身边带着他从保险柜里找到的盒子。他发现密码盒是空的。他接到韦尔内打来的电话,韦尔内急切地想拿回盒子,以确保银行的声誉不会受到损害。

综述:第90章

在庄园里,科莱发现谷仓里的电脑分别监听了包括雅克·索尼埃在内的五个人。其他四人也都是重要人物,甚至包括了法国情报局局长。特工们还在现场发现了示意图,它显示窃听器就藏在索尼埃桌子上的骑士模型里。

Summary: Chapter 91

Silas and Rémy have put Teabing in the back of the limo. The Teacher calls Silas and says that Rémy will bring him the keystone so he can be "dealt with." The Teacher tells Rémy where to drop Silas and where to meet the Teacher. Rémy thinks Silas will be gotten rid of. He laughs to himself at the way the Teacher has used the Bishop and Silas as pawns.

Summary: Chapter 92

At Kings College, where the religious research database is housed, Sophie and Langdon speak with Pamela Gettum, who agrees to help them use the database. They show her only the first two lines of the poem and ask her to search for a knight who was buried by a pope in London. The search turns up too much data, and they have to show her the second two lines of the poem. She realizes that their search is related to the Grail and laughs at the number of Grail hunters who have come into her library. She starts a new search and tells them it will take fifteen minutes.

Summary: Chapter 93

Silas goes to the Opus Dei house in London, where he is welcomed by the numerary at the door and given a room. The numerary gets a call from the London police, who ask if an albino monk has been let into the house. When the numerary says yes, the police tell him not to alert the monk. They say they will be over immediately.

Summary: Chapter 94

Rémy meets the Teacher in St. James Park and accepts

综述:第 91 章

塞拉斯和雷米将提彬放入豪华轿车的后背箱。导师打电话给塞拉斯,说楔石由雷米交给他,以便他可以"处理"雷米。导师又告诉雷米在哪里放下塞拉斯,以及在何处与他会面。雷米认为塞拉斯已经毫无用处了,他暗笑主教和塞拉斯都是被导师利用的棋子。

综述:第 92 章

国王学院里有一个宗教研究数据库,索菲和兰登请帕美拉·杰塔姆帮助他们使用数据库,她同意了。他们先给她看了诗的前两行,希望她能搜索到一个埋葬于伦敦并由教皇主持礼葬的骑士。由于搜索出的资料过多,他们只好又给她看了接下来的两行。她意识到他们的搜索与圣杯有关,笑称有很多探寻圣杯的人到他们的图书馆来。她开始了新的搜索,告诉他们只需15 分钟。

综述:第 93 章

塞拉斯来到伦敦的天主事工会活动中心,一个独身会员在门口迎接他并给了他一个房间。那个独身会员接到伦敦警察局的电话,问他们是否接收了一个修道士。独身会员说确有此事,警察告诉他不要惊动他,他们马上就到。

综述:第 94 章

雷米在圣詹姆斯公园与导师会面,他喝了一些教

some cognac from his flask. The drink contains peanut dust, which Rémy is allergic to. Rémy slowly dies. The Teacher reflects on how unfair it was that knew immediately which tomb Saunière meant, since he had been bugging Saunière's office and knew of his respect for this particular knight. Meanwhile, Bishop Aringarosa leaves the airport and is met by a British police deputy, who says that Fache told him to take Aringarosa to Scotland Yard. In the car, Aringarosa hears Opus Dei's address being broadcast over the scanner. He demands that the officer take him there instead.

Summary: Chapter 95

At King's College, Sophie and Langdon look at several results for their latest search before hitting on a book about Sir Isaac Newton. Langdon realizes that Newton is probably the knight they're looking for. He was buried in London, was a knight, and was buried by Alexander Pope, the writer.

Analysis: Chapters 89–95

At this point, it isn't clear how much Fache understands or knows about the mythology behind the treasure hunt that the three are now engaged in. He may or may not understand the meaning of the password (Sofia) on the first cryptex.

The Teacher's phone calls to Rémy and Silas are confusing. It's impossible to know whether Rémy or Silas is correct about the Teacher's true intentions. The tension surrounding the identity of the Teacher is reaching the breaking point. Whoever he is, the Teacher is clearly a man capable of understanding his minions' deeper motivations—for Silas, faith and for Rémy, money—and manipulating them.

主瓶里的白兰地。由于酒里含有雷米过敏的花生粉，雷米慢慢地死了。导师心想他的优势别人简直难以比拟，因为他一直在索尼埃的办公室安有窃听器，当他得知索尼埃对一位骑士尤其尊敬时，他立即明白了索尼埃所指的坟墓是哪一座。与此同时，阿林加洛沙主教从机场出来，一位英国警官代法希来接他，并说法希让他把他送到苏格兰场。在车上，阿林加洛沙听到扫描器里播报天主事工会活动中心的地址，于是他让警官改道将他送往那里。

综述：第95章

在国王学院，索菲和兰登看着最新搜索出的一些结果，偶然发现了一本关于艾萨克·牛顿爵士的书。兰登意识到牛顿或许就是他们要找的骑士。他葬于伦敦，身为爵士，并由作家亚历山大·蒲柏为其主持葬礼。

品评：第89~95章

目前，法希对于他们三人现在从事的寻宝活动背后的神话有多少了解尚不清楚。他或许明白第一个密码盒上的密码(Sofia)，但也可能并不理解。

导师打给雷米和塞拉斯的电话令人困惑。我们无从得知究竟是雷米还是塞拉斯对导师真正意图的揣测是正确的。导师身份之谜也在其呼之欲出的前一刻达到了顶点。无论他是谁，毫无疑问，他能洞悉部下的深层动机——对塞拉斯来说是信仰而对于雷米则是金钱——并将他们玩弄于股掌之中。

Pamela Gettum's reference to the many people who come into her library looking for the Grail is a reminder that the secrets of the Grail are open secrets—secrets many people know but few are willing to acknowledge openly. In the case of the Grail, the problem is that many people suspect the substance of the secret but haven't been able to act upon their suspicions because they do not have proof.

Silas states a desire to purge the sins of the last twenty-four hours in his cell. His desire sounds almost ridiculous because he has committed so many sins, murder being the most serious. But within the spiritual calculus that Silas has learned, any act can be excused if it is meant to lead to a desirable end, and any act can be purged from one's spiritual record with appropriate prayer and punishment. Silas's beliefs suggest the kind of religious justification for violence that characterizes fundamentalist and terrorist movements.

In the process of finding information about Sir Isaac Newton, Langdon delivers a short lecture on tarot cards and their function as storytellers about the Magdalene legend. Langdon's lectures, which concern information, not judgment, seem to have no place in a world divided into those who have faith in the current Church and those who have faith in a different order. Langdon does not seem to realize that he can't avoid taking sides on this issue.

Chapters 96–101

Summary: Chapter 96

Silas wakes up with the sense that something is wrong. He sees the police car outside the building and realizes that

帕美拉·杰塔姆提到有很多人到图书馆查询圣杯,这暗示了圣杯的秘密其实是公开的秘密——很多人都知道这些秘密，但只是很少有人愿意公然地承认。在圣杯这件事上,很多人都对这个秘密的真实性提出了质疑,但却找不到证据来证明。

塞拉斯在他狭小的房间里,表达了希望可以洗清他在过去的24小时里犯下的罪孽的愿望。他的愿望听起来几乎是荒谬可笑的,因为他已犯下了太多的罪行,其中以凶杀最为严重。但是按照塞拉斯所学的精神记量法,如果是为了达到值得的目标,那么任何行为都是可以被饶恕的,而且只要经过适当的祈祷和惩罚,任何行为都可以从精神记录中清洗掉。塞拉斯的这些信仰暗示了原教旨主义和恐怖主义运动中典型的以宗教为暴力做辩护的行为。

在查找艾萨克·牛顿爵士的信息的过程中，兰登做了一个关于占卜纸牌以及它们有作为抹大拉传说叙述者作用的短小演说。兰登的演说关注的是信息而非判断,这在一个分化为信仰当前教会和其他不同秩序的世界里似乎是站不住脚的。兰登似乎还没有意识到,在这个问题上他不可避免地要选择自己的立场。

第96~101章

综述:第96章

塞拉斯醒来后感觉事情有些不对劲。他看到楼外

the police are looking for him. In the process of fleeing the building, he accidentally shoots Bishop Aringarosa.

Summary: Chapter 97

At Westminster Abbey, Langdon and Sophie look for Newton's tomb. Meanwhile, the Teacher stands outside Newton's tomb with the cryptex. He doesn't understand what orb the riddle refers to. When he sees Sophie and Langdon looking for Newton's tomb, he realizes that Langdon might be able to help him decipher the final clue. He formulates a plan to force Langdon to comply.

Summary: Chapter 98

Langdon and Sophie go to Newton's tomb and see that there are many orbs on it. Sophie sees a message from the Teacher scrawled on the floor. The message says he has Teabing and wants to meet Sophie and Langdon in the garden. In their haste to get there, Sophie and Langdon miss the sign saying that that area is under renovation. When they arrive at the route to the garden, they see that there is no exit. A door closes, and they are trapped—with Teabing, who is pointing a revolver at them.

Summary: Chapter 99

Teabing explains his treachery. Saunière refused to reveal the Grail because he had been threatened by the Church. The Church had killed the rest of Sophie's family and promised to kill Sophie if the documents were revealed. Teabing orchestrated Saunière's death and the deaths of the other three members of the Brotherhood. Because Sophie understood Saunière's

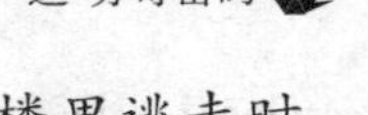

的警车，意识到警察正在搜捕他。当他从楼里逃走时，意外地射中了阿林加洛沙主教。

综述：第 97 章

兰登和索菲在威斯敏斯特教堂寻找牛顿的墓室。与此同时，导师正拿着密码盒站在牛顿墓室的外面，但他想不出谜语中所指的圆球究竟是哪一个。这时他看到了正在寻找牛顿墓室的索菲和兰登，心想兰登或许可以帮他破解这条最后的线索。于是他制定了一个计划，以迫使兰登就范。

综述：第 98 章

兰登和索菲来到牛顿的墓室，看到那里有很多圆球体。索菲发现一条导师写在地上的信息，上面说提彬在他手上，他要在花园见他们。索菲和兰登匆忙赶往花园，没注意到写有此区正在整修的告示牌。他们来到通往花园的路，却发现那里没有出口。门关上了，他们被困在里面——提彬用左轮手枪对准了他们。

综述：第 99 章

提彬对他的背叛做了解释。索尼埃因为受到教会的威胁而拒绝揭示圣杯的秘密。教会杀死了索菲的家人，并说如果圣杯文献被公布他们必将杀死索菲。提彬精心策划，杀害了索尼埃以及其他三个兄弟会成员。因为索菲明白索尼埃的密码，他决定在到达他设

codes, he decided to keep Sophie and Langdon involved in the quest until the rendezvous at Temple Church, where he was going to steal the cryptex. Teabing asks Sophie and Langdon to help him find the Grail. Sophie swears she will not, because Teabing killed her grandfather. Teabing asks Langdon what he will do.

Summary: Chapter 100

Aringarosa, who lies on the ground outside Opus Dei's house, remembers the meeting he had five months ago with the Pope's secretary at Castel Gandolfo. The assembled officials told him that Opus Dei was to be severed from the Church by order of the Pope himself. The Church had become embarrassed by its affiliation with the sect because of Opus Dei's aggressive recruiting practices, treatment of women, and habits of bodily mortification. Not wanting to embarrass Aringarosa and his order, they gave him six months to effect the separation himself. Shortly after that, the Teacher called Aringarosa and told him he had information that would lead to the discovery of a relic that would give him great power within the Church.

Silas, frantic, brings Aringarosa to the hospital. The doctor tells him that the bishop may be dying.

Summary: Chapter 101

By Newton's tomb, Langdon tries to buy time by staring out the window and pretending to think about the password. He realizes that the password must be apple—the sign of Isaac Newton, and the symbol of Eve's fall. He opens the cryptex, takes out the map inside, and then tells Teabing that he knows

定好的圣殿教堂以前继续让索菲和兰登参与探索，到时再盗取密码盒。提彬要索菲和兰登帮他找出圣杯。索菲发誓决不帮他，因为他杀死了她的祖父。提彬问兰登做何打算。

综述：第 100 章

阿林加洛沙躺在天主事工会外的地上，想起了 5 个月前他与教皇秘书在岗道尔夫堡的会面。一众官员告诉他教皇将亲自下命将天主事工会革除出教会，因为天主事工会过于大胆的招收教徒的行为、对待妇女的政策以及肉体苦修的做法已使教会感到与此教派的联系很难堪。为了不至于使阿林加洛沙和他的组织太难堪，他们给他 6 个月的时间主动与教会分离。此后不久，导师打电话给阿林加洛沙，说他有一条能够找到一个遗迹的信息，这可以使他在教会中获得巨大的权力。

狂乱的塞拉斯把阿林加洛沙送到医院。医生告诉他主教恐怕不行了。

综述：第 101 章

在牛顿的坟墓旁，兰登注视着窗外，假装正在思考密码，希望以此争取一些时间。他意识到密码一定是苹果——艾萨克·牛顿的标志，也是夏娃堕落的象征。他打开密码盒，取出了里面的地图，然后告诉提彬

the password. He lets a flicker of doubt cross his face, so that Teabing thinks he is bluffing. Then he throws the cryptex, which he has put back together, up toward the dome. Teabing tries desperately to catch it, but the glass inside breaks. Langdon then reveals that he has the map. By this time, Teabing is disarmed and lying on the floor. Fache comes to the chamber and apprehends Teabing, who screams for Langdon to tell him what the map says as he is led away by.

Analysis: Chapters 96–101

Silas's pre-Aringarosa self, the self that was governed by violence and instinct, seems about to prevail and save him. Instead, it ends up causing him to shoot the Bishop. This unfortunate outcome suggests that once one has decided to use violence for any reason, as Silas has decided to use violence in the service of God, one must be prepared to see that violence erupt in unexpected, undesired ways.

Teabing's anger at not being able to figure out the cryptex's password is reminiscent of something Teabing said to Silas when he wanted to steal the first cryptex: "Only the pure of heart can open that, and you will not be able to." Teabing, who is not pure of heart, can't open the cryptex. The situation hearkens back to the legend of King Arthur and the sword, in which only Arthur, the pure of heart, could release the sword from the rock into which it was plunged.

At the moment of truth, Teabing reveals his motivations and machinations. Brown had hinted that the members of Opus Dei were the ones who wanted to find the cryptex so that they could bury the information even further, but it turns out Teabing was the one who wanted the cryptex. And far from

他知道密码了。他脸上闪过了一丝不确定的神色,这让提彬觉得他是在虚张声势。紧接着,兰登把重新扣好的密码盒抛向了拱顶,提彬拼命地想要接住它,但里面的玻璃还是碎了。兰登随后宣称他已经得到了地图。此时,提彬躺在地上,并且没了武器。法希进入大厅,逮捕了提彬。当他被带走时,他声嘶力竭地叫兰登告诉他地图的内容。

品评:第96~101章

本我已被暴力和本能钳制的塞拉斯完全跪拜在阿林加洛沙主教的脚下,这似乎能够让他取得成功并获得救赎。相反,最终却导致他射中了主教。这个不幸的结果反映出一旦一个人决定使用暴力,无论出于什么原因,即使像塞拉斯那样以侍奉上帝之名而施暴,他们都必须准备好面对暴力以意想不到的、违背本愿的方式爆发。

提彬因无法破解密码盒的密码而恼怒,这使人想起了当他想偷第一个密码盒时他对塞拉斯说的话:"只有纯净的心灵才能打开它,而你做不到。"提彬的心灵并不纯净,因此他也无法打开密码盒。这一情节影射了亚瑟王与剑的传说——只有心灵纯净的亚瑟才能拔出插在岩石间的剑。

在真相大白的时刻,提彬将他的动机和诡计都和盘托出。布朗曾暗示天主事工会的人想得到密码盒,以便把其中的秘密更深地埋藏起来,但人们最终发现想得到密码盒的竟然是提彬。他不是要保守这个秘密,而是要将其公之于众。尽管整部小说给读者的印

wanting to keep the secret, he wanted to bring it to light. Although the reader has been told throughout the novel that openness is desirable, Teabing's bloody quest casts doubt on the virtues of revealing secrets. In the moral universe of *The Da Vinci Code*, no amount of innocent blood is acceptable. In this context, Teabing's actions are insane.

Just as Saunière set up the puzzle that Sophie and Langdon had to crack in order to find the Grail, Brown sets up a puzzle for us: who is the mysterious Teacher? Saunière's puzzle concerned both the characters and the readers, but the puzzle of the Teacher's identity is the readers' alone to solve. Sophie and Langdon aren't trying to find out who the Teacher is, because they don't even know he exists. Moreover, they trust Teabing—perhaps too much—and do not suspect him of anything. Teabing's jocularity and eagerness to help Sophie and Langdon won them over completely. The readers, in turn, fell for the distracting Opus Dei story line and decided that they, or some other Catholic sect, must be behind the Teacher.

The fact that the Church wanted to sever its connection with Opus Dei forces a reevaluation of the Church's motives. The Church has been portrayed as the enemy, but it seems the Church is actually attempting to modernize itself by rejecting sects like Opus Dei. In the final chapters, Brown reveals that the Church isn't actually the enemy.

Chapter 102–Epilogue

Summary: Chapter 102

Silas, wounded by a bullet in his chest, sits in Kensington Gardens. He prays for Bishop Aringarosa and for forgiveness

象都是秘密应该被公开,但提彬的血腥追寻却使人们对揭示秘密的道德性产生了怀疑。在《达·芬奇密码》的道德世界里,任何无辜的牺牲都是不能接受的。在这种背景之下,提彬的行为无比疯狂。

当索尼埃为索菲和兰登设下为找到圣杯而必须破解的谜题时,布朗也为我们设置了一道谜题:神秘的导师是谁?故事中的人物和读者共同面对着索尼埃的谜题,而导师的身份之谜则只能由读者自己破解。索菲和兰登不会去试图找出导师是谁,因为他们甚至不知道他的存在。而且他们信任提彬——或许过于相信了——因而从未怀疑过他任何事情。提彬的滑稽诙谐和热心帮助完全征服了索菲和兰登。至于读者则被天主事工会的故事线索转移了视线,并且相信一定是天主事工会或其他的天主教教派在背后支持导师。

教会希望切断与天主事工会的联系的事实使人不得不重新评估教会的目的。教会一直被描绘成敌人,但它似乎正通过革除诸如天主事工会这样的教派使其自身现代化。在最后几章里,布朗揭示出教会事实上并非敌人。

第102章~尾声

综述:第102章

胸部中枪的塞拉斯坐在肯辛顿花园里。他为阿林加洛沙主教祈祷并祈祷上帝的宽恕和怜悯。临死之

and mercy. Before he dies, he feels in his heart that his Lord is good and merciful.

Summary: Chapter 103

Fache, leaving an interrogation of Teabing, goes to visit Aringarosa. Aringarosa is despondent at Silas's death and the news that he killed the four brothers and the nun in Paris. Aringarosa asks Fache to distribute the money he planned to pay the Teacher amongst the families of the five people that Silas killed.

Summary: Chapter 104

Sophie and Langdon arrive at Rosslyn Chapel in Scotland. The inside of the cryptex contained a phrase directing them to Rosslyn, which had been built by the Knights Templar. For years, people have thought that Rosslyn might be where the Grail is held, but it's never been proven. In the chapel, Sophie looks up at one of the arches. She knows she has seen it before. When she was very young, she fell asleep looking at the arch and woke up in time to see her grandfather saying goodbye to somebody who was on the porch of a nearby house. Sophie wanders toward the house.

The docent asks Langdon where he got the box, saying his grandfather made the same one for his grandmother. The docent lost his grandfather, parents, and sister in a car accident.

Sophie enters the house and finds her grandmother. The two women embrace. Sophie's brother, the docent, comes into the house and embraces them both.

前，他内心感到上帝是和蔼仁慈的。

综述：第103章

审讯提彬时，法希抽身离开，前去探视阿林加洛沙。塞拉斯的死以及他在巴黎杀害了四个兄弟会成员和一个修女的消息让阿林加洛沙感到沮丧。阿林加洛沙让法希把他准备付给导师的钱分发给五个被塞拉斯杀害的死者的家属。

综述：第104章

索菲和兰登来到位于苏格兰的罗斯林教堂。罗斯林教堂由圣殿骑士所建，密码盒中的一个词指引他们来到了这里。很久以来，人们一直认为圣杯可能就收藏在罗斯林教堂，只是从未被证实过。在礼拜堂，索菲抬头看到一个拱门，她想起她以前见过它。在她还很小时，她看着那拱门就睡着了，醒来时正看到她的祖父在附近一栋房子的走廊上和一个人道别。于是索菲朝那栋房子走去。

讲解员问兰登从哪里得到这个盒子的，他说他的祖父曾给他的祖母做过一个一模一样的盒子。讲解员的祖父、父母和姐姐都在一次车祸中去世了。

索菲走进房子，在那里她见到了她的祖母，她们紧紧地拥抱在一起。索菲的弟弟，也就是那个讲解员，也走了进来，和他们拥抱在一起。

Summary: Chapter 105

Marie Chauvel tells Langdon the story of how the family separated. Sophie's parents were of the blood line of Jesus and Mary, but they had changed their names for safety. Supposedly, they were in a car accident, but the grandparents suspected it was not actually an accident. They faked the deaths of the grandmother and Sophie's brother, both of whom went into hiding in Scotland.

Langdon wants to know whether the Grail is really at Rosslyn, and Marie reads him the verse again. She says she doesn't know whether or not it is, and she says the secret is not necessarily meant to be revealed. One day, she says, the meaning of the verse will dawn on Langdon, and he will then have to keep the secret. In the meantime, the Priory is ready to appoint new brothers to the brotherhood and start guarding the secret anew. She goes back inside and Sophie comes out. Sophie and Langdon go to walk in the fields. They kiss and agree to meet in Florence in a month.

Summary: Epilogue

Back in Paris, Langdon realizes the meaning of Saunière's poem. He runs to the Louvre, where a giant inverted pyramid hovers over another, smaller pyramid built into the floor of the museum. He realizes that these two pyramids represent the Chalice and the Blade, the ancient symbols of female and male mentioned in the lines of the poem. In his manuscript, he had described the smaller pyramid as similar to the tip of an underground vault. He now realizes that his speculation was actually the truth, and that is why Saunière must have told Sophie to find him. He falls to his knees in front of the smaller pyramid.

综述:第105章

玛丽·肖维尔向兰登讲述了一家人是如何分离的。索菲的父母是耶稣基督和玛利亚的血脉,但出于安全的考虑,他们更改了姓氏。据推测,他们死于车祸,但祖父和祖母怀疑那实际上并非意外。他们制造了祖母和索菲弟弟死亡的假象,两人隐居在苏格兰。

兰登想知道圣杯是不是真的在罗斯林教堂,玛丽给他又读了一遍那首诗。她说她也不知道它是否在这里,而且她并没有打算公开秘密。她说,终有一天兰登会领会到诗中的含义,到时他必须要保守秘密。与此同时,郇山隐修会已准备好委派新的护卫长担当新一轮的秘密守卫职责。她回到房中,索菲走了出来。索菲和兰登来到田间散步,他们亲吻对方并相约一个月后在佛罗伦萨见面。

综述:尾声

回到巴黎后,兰登明白了索尼埃诗中的含义。他跑到卢浮宫,在那里,一个巨大的倒立形金字塔旋亘于另一个塔身建于博物馆地下的更小的金字塔上面。他意识到这两个金字塔代表着圣杯和剑刃,正是诗文中提及的古代女性和男性的象征。在他的书稿中,他曾描绘过这个稍小的金字塔像是一个地下拱顶的顶部。现在他明白了他的推测正与事实相符,这也是索尼埃为什么告诉索菲一定要找到他的原因。最后兰登跪拜在小金字塔的前面。

Analysis: Chapter 102–Epilogue

Even Opus Dei, which has had a totally negative image throughout the novel, is redeemed when Silas experiences a feeling of purity and knowledge of mercy. Now that it's clear that the Teacher, and not Bishop Aringarosa, told Silas to kill, Opus Dei has shed some of its taint of blood.

The fundamental goodness of the Bishop and Fache, like Silas's experience praying before death in the Garden, portrays religious people in a good light. Though the Church has come in for quite a beating in the rest of the novel, in the end, Brown makes it clear that some aspects of religion are positive, and some religious people are good people.

The bucolic setting of the chapter set at Rosslyn Chapel, when contrasted with the darkness of the novels' other settings, echoes our satisfaction at emerging from the darkness of confusion into the light of understanding. For hours now, Sophie and Langdon have been in dark places: the Louvre in the middle of the night, cars racing through darkened parks and fields, a bank after hours, Teabing's chateau at three o'clock in the morning., and the forbidding Temple Church. Rosslyn Chapel, with its springtime feeling and country setting, parallels Sophie's happy discovery that some of her family is, after all, alive.

Unlike Teabing, who let the quest for the Grail take over his life and drive him to murder, Sophie never expressed a need to see the Grail. She was more concerned with the desire to see her family again than with the specific location of the documents and sarcophagus. Marie Chauvel had been able to live close to the secret of the Grail—in the form of her husband—for years, without having to see it for herself. Langdon

品评:第 102 章 ~ 尾声

小说中一直以反面形象出现的天主事工会,在塞拉斯经历了心灵的净化并体会到上帝的怜悯时得到了救赎。既然现在已经清楚是导师而非阿林加洛沙主教教唆塞拉斯杀人,那么天主事工会就可以擦去它身上的部分血污了。

主教和法希本性的善良以及塞拉斯死前在花园所做的祈祷描绘出宗教人士美好的一面。尽管教会在小说中一直备受鞭挞,但在结尾部分,布朗还是明确表示了宗教的某些方面是积极的,而一些宗教人士也都是好人。

本章的背景设置在了田园牧歌般的罗斯林教堂,与小说中的其他黑暗场景形成了鲜明对比,这正应和了我们从迷茫的黑暗走向豁然开朗的惬意心情。之前的几个小时里,索菲和兰登一直处于黑暗之中:从午夜的卢浮宫,驱车驶过黑漆漆的公园和田野,数小时后来到银行,凌晨三点到达提彬的庄园,再到令人生畏的圣殿教堂。一派田园风光的罗斯林教堂让人如浴春风,而更让索菲倍感欣喜的是她发现她的一些亲人还活着。

寻找圣杯占据了提彬的整个生活,他甚至为此而行凶杀人;索菲则不同,她从未想过要找到圣杯。与找到圣杯文献和石棺的确切位置相比,她更关心、更渴望的是与亲人的重逢。多年来,由于丈夫的缘故,玛丽·肖维尔的生活一直与圣杯的秘密密切相关,但是她本人并未见过圣杯。兰登一直站在故事中那些执迷

has always stood in contrast to those in the story who are obsessed with the location of the Grail, but in these final chapters, he shows that he is not immune to the mystery and charm of the Grail. When he finally finds the place where the Grail must be hidden, he falls to his knees in worship. It is a striking departure from the sort of professorial interest he shows in the rest of the novel. In the presence of the Grail, Robert Langdon seems to have discovered the value of faith.

于找到圣杯的人的反面，但在最后几章中，他好像也无法抵御圣杯的神秘魅力。当他最终找到圣杯的隐藏之地时，他以崇敬之心向它施以跪拜。这与他在小说的其他部分所表现出的以学术研究为目的的兴趣有着天壤之别。在圣杯面前，罗伯特·兰登似乎已经明白了信仰的意义。

断章·取义

IMPORTANT QUOTATIONS EXPLAINED

1. As someone who had spent his life exploring the hidden interconnectivity of disparate emblems and ideologies, Langdon viewed the world as a web of profoundly intertwined histories and events. The connections may be invisible, he often preached to his symbology classes at Harvard, but they are always there, buried just beneath the surface.

With this statement, Langdon describes a major theme of the novel—the idea that secrets lie all around us awaiting interpretation. From the beginning of the novel, when Saunière leaves a mass of secrets and puzzles around his body, explicit examples of puzzles and codes abound. Some of the puzzles and codes are known to Langdon already, through his studies, and some are not.

Other connections that are buried just beneath the surface are the pieces of knowledge that the characters need in order to solve the mysteries. These pieces of knowledge are already known to the characters, but they must remember them and fit them together in the right way. Langdon is continually experiencing revelations. For example, he suddenly remembers that the Knights Templar worshipped a "head stone" of a god named Baphomet. Another time, he realizes that Saunière was referring to the apple when he named the orb that should have been on Newton's tomb. Sophie is also in the habit of suddenly remembering important information. At the end of the nov-

语出·有因

1. 作为一个终生都在探索孤立的象征符号或观念之间隐含的相关性的人，兰登把这个世界视为一张由历史和事件相互交织而成的深不可测的大网。他经常在哈佛的符号学课上鼓吹说，各种关联性也许看不到，但它们却一直在那儿，伏在表层下面。

通过这段陈述，兰登阐述了这部小说的一个重要主题——秘密就在身边，等待我们的解读。从小说的开篇，索尼埃在他的尸体旁留下诸多秘密和谜题开始，各种具体形式的谜语和密码便纷至沓来。通过研究，兰登解开了其中的一些谜语和密码，但其余的一些他也弄不明白。

其他一些埋藏在表象之下的联系则是故事人物要解开谜团应具有的知识片段。这些知识片段已然存在于他们的脑中，但还须他们记起并以正确的方式拼接在一起。兰登不断地想起一些事情，例如他突然想到圣殿骑士膜拜的基石就是鲍芙默神。另一次，他意识到索尼埃所说的圆球指的是苹果，它应该就在牛顿的墓穴里。索菲也常常会记起一些重要的信息。在小说结尾，她想起了她小时候和祖父来过罗斯林教堂，还看到过祖父与祖母谈话。按照布朗的描述，这些事情一直都在索菲的记忆中，只是需要适当的刺激来触

el, she recalls that she saw her grandfather talking to her grandmother when she was younger and they were visiting Rosslyn Chapel. According to Brown, Sophie remembered this all along and just needed the right impetus to uncover it.

2. God whispers in his ear, one agent had insisted after a particularly impressive display of Fache's sixth sense. Collet had to admit, if there was a God, Bezu Fache would be on his A-list. The captain attended mass and confession with zealous regularity—far more than the requisite holiday attendance fulfilled by other officials in the name of good public relations.

This description of the French Judicial Police Chief's supernatural sixth sense is an example of the false clues and mysteries that Dan Brown sprinkles throughout the text. This paragraph comes early in the novel, and it plants the idea that Fache, who has at this point made a dramatic effort to arrest Langdon for the murder of Saunière, might be involved with an evil force such as Opus Dei or the Church itself. The cross that Fache wears is mentioned, as is the fact that he lost a lot of money recently in speculating on technology. The reader is meant to think that Fache might be involved with the Church and the killings for reasons of money and faith. Later, Brown reveals that Fache had nothing to do with Saunière's killings, and that the insinuations of Fache's guilt were a red herring meant to throw us off of Teabing's trail.

This passage also highlights a fundamental problem of the typical thriller novel. In literary novels, characters develop slowly. In thrillers, character development is sometimes sacri-

发它们。

2. 有一次，在法希展示了那令人敬佩的第六感以后，一位特工人员坚持说有上帝在法希耳畔嘀咕。科莱不得不承认，如果有上帝的话，贝祖·法希肯定会上他的甲等选民名单。法希以极大的热情参加弥撒和忏悔——与从事公共事务的其他官员只在假日必须参加时才参加相比，他去得要经常、有规律得多。

丹·布朗在文中穿插了许多虚假的线索和谜团，这段关于法国司法警察局长的神奇的第六感的描述便是其中之一。小说开篇部分的这段描述使读者感觉，现在正千方百计以谋杀索尼埃的罪名逮捕兰登的法希或许与诸如天主事工会或天主教会本身的某个邪恶势力有染。文中还提到了法希佩戴的十字架以及他最近在科技投资方面损失了一大笔钱，因此读者会认为，法希或许是因为钱和信仰的原因才参与了教会的谋杀行动。在后文中，布朗揭示了法希与索尼埃的死毫无关联，对于法希有罪的种种暗示只是为了转移人们的视线，而不至于去怀疑提彬。

这段文字还集中反映了典型的惊悚小说的一个基本问题。文学小说中的人物往往有一个逐渐丰满的过程，而惊悚小说中的人物有时则要服务于悬念的制

ficed for the sake of suspense. Bezu Fache, who functions largely as a false clue, does not have depth of personality. After Brown strips away the reader's bad impression of him, almost no impression is left at all.

3. "History is always written by the winners. When two cultures clash, the loser is obliterated, and the winner writes the history books—books which glorify their own cause and disparage the conquered foe. As Napoleon once said, 'What is history, but a fable agreed upon?'"

Although this theory is advanced by Leigh Teabing, who is later found to be unreliable and mentally unbalanced, Langdon agrees with it. The idea of history as a story written by winners is the fundamental underpinning of *The Da Vinci Code*. Throughout the narrative, Brown expounds on the ideas that Langdon and Teabing work with professionally: certain gospels were left out of the Bible because of the political desires of leaders; Mary Magdalene was of the royal blood of Benjamin and more likely was Jesus' wife rather than a prostitute; pagans were killed in order to further the political goals of the Church; and the meanings of certain words and symbols were changed in order to force people to change their beliefs.

In this case Brown is essentially the rewriter of history. It is tempting to believe every theory he advances simply because each theory opposes conventional wisdom, which suggests that Brown is uncovering hidden truths. But some of the ideas presented as fact by Langdon and Teabing are enormously complex, and so little proof backs them up that it would be hard to believe them.

造。贝祖·法希的个性并没有被太深地挖掘，他的主要作用是引出一条错误的线索。当布朗告诉读者法希不是坏人时，读者会感觉除此以外对他没有什么印象。

3. “历史总是由胜利者来谱写的。当两个文明交锋时，失败者的文明史就会被删除，胜利者会重新编写历史来颂扬自己而贬低被征服者。正如拿破仑所说‘什么是历史？只不过是编造的谎言罢了。’”

尽管我们将在后文中看到提彬是一个不可信且神经错乱的人，但他提出的这一理论兰登也表示赞同。历史是由胜利者编造的故事这一观点是《达·芬奇密码》的一个基本支柱。布朗在整个叙述中详加阐释的这些观点，兰登和提彬从专业角度进行了研究：基于某些统治者的政治需要，福音书中的一些内容并未收入《圣经》之中；玛利亚·抹大拉是本杰明家族的王室后裔，她很可能是耶稣基督的妻子而不是一个妓女；教会是为了进一步达到他们的政治目的而杀害异教徒；一些文字以及符号的意义被篡改，以迫使人们改变信仰。

在这种情况下，布朗事实上已经重写了历史。我们很容易会对布朗提出的每个理论都信以为真，只是因为它们颠覆了我们一贯认为的常识，好像他揭示的正是一些被埋藏的真相。但兰登和提彬提出的一些他们认为是事实的观点却相当复杂，而且缺乏证据的支持，难以令人信服。

4. Silas could feel his homeland testing him, drawing violent memories from his redeemed soul. You have been reborn, he reminded himself. His service to God today had required the sin of murder, and it was a sacrifice Silas knew he would have to hold silently in his heart for all eternity.

Silas stands for the capacity of the Church to change people completely, an important idea in the novel. The Church made a concerted effort to erase people's belief in the divinity of women and nature, stressed the idea of female original sin, and promoted the ultimate authority of the Church. The Church is so successful at changing entire societies that it can take commonly held ideas—such as the idea that sex is something to enjoy—and turn them into taboos. Brown suggests that Sophie's horror and disgust at seeing her grandfather in the act of sex is a product of the culture she grew up in, not a fundamental human instinct.

In order to prove that the Church, and faith itself, can change the way men operate, Brown demonstrates how faith and Bishop Aringarosa's attention give purpose to the murderous Silas. All the Church does, however, is give Silas an excuse for killing. Silas justifies murder by telling himself he is killing in the name of God. He does not hesitate when the Teacher asks him to kill people in the name of finding the Grail and (he thinks) saving Opus Dei. Silas has come to believe that the Church and God are so important that any action taken on their behalf is acceptable.

4. 塞拉斯感到他的祖国在考验着他，正从他被救赎的灵魂中拉扯出狂乱的记忆来。你已经再生，他提醒自己。今天，因要侍奉上帝，他不得不犯谋杀之罪。赛拉斯知道这个牺牲他将会永远默默地藏在心里。

塞拉斯体现了教会具备彻底改变一个人的能力，这也是这部小说所传达的一个重要理念。教会合力抹煞人们心中关于女性和自然神圣性的信仰，而灌输女性原罪的思想，并促使教会成为绝对权威。教会成功地改变了整个社会，它将像"性是一种愉悦"这种人们普遍拥有的观念统统变成了禁忌。布朗暗示，索菲在看到她祖父的性行为时所产生的恐惧和反感正是她成长所在文化环境的产物，而非基本的人类本能。

为了证明教会和信仰本身能够改变人们的行为方式，布朗讲述了信仰以及主教的关注是如何为塞拉斯的杀人行为注入决心和毅力的。教会给塞拉斯的不过是一个杀人的借口，而他则告诉自己他正在以上帝之名杀人，以此为他的谋杀行为开脱。所以当导师以寻找圣杯之名要他杀人时，他毫无迟疑，并认为这可以拯救天主事工会。塞拉斯相信教会和上帝是如此重要，任何以他们的名义进行的行为都是允许的。

5. "*The Bible represents a fundamental guidepost for millions of people on the planet, in much the same way the Koran, Torah, and Pali Canon offer guidance to people of other religions. If you and I could dig up documentation that contradicted the holy stories of Islamic belief, Judaic belief, Buddhist belief, pagan belief, should we do that? Should we wave a flag and tell the Buddhists that the Buddha did not come from a lotus blossom? Or that Jesus was not born of a literal virgin birth? Those who truly understand their faiths understand the stories are metaphorical.*"

Langdon, who speaks these words, thinks that ignorance is sometimes preferable to harsh truths. Langdon is an academic and a religious scholar, not a man of the Church, so to some degree he can hold himself apart from controversy over religious doctrine. Unlike Teabing, he has refused to judge Christians who believe that Jesus was the son of God and therefore could never have been married, and that Mary Magdalene was a prostitute. He sees the secret of Jesus' life as one that could probably lie undiscovered for years without any particular poor effect on the world.

In this quotation, Langdon refuses to politicize religion. He believes that people who have faith should be allowed to have it, because they're not hurting anybody. Langdon's statement seems at odds with other stories he tells in the course of the novel. It is he who mentions women being burned at the stake for helping other women give birth without pain, and tells of the paintings of Da Vinci that were painted over because they were inconsistent with the teachings of the Church. Perhaps this quotation is an attempt, however inconsistent with Langdon's character, to provide a counterpoint to Teabing's fanaticism.

5. “《圣经》给居住在这个星球上成千上万的人们设置了一个最根本的路标，可兰经犹太律法，还有巴利教规，也以完全相同的方式给信仰其他宗教的人们指点迷津。假如你我能找到一些与伊斯兰教、犹太教、佛教以及异教的传说相背离的材料，我们会那样做吗？我们会挥舞着手中的旗帜，对那些佛教徒说，我们能证明佛主不是从莲花里生出来的吗？或者告诉那些基督徒，耶稣不是从处女的子宫里孕育出来的吗？那些真正理解自身信仰的人，通常也知道这些故事传说是隐喻性的。”

做出上述评述的兰登认为，有时候在无情的真相面前保持一点无知未尝不是一件好事。兰登是一个从学术角度研究宗教的学者，而不是教会人士，这使得他在某种程度上在探讨宗教教义问题时可以置身事外。与提彬不同的是，对于那些相信耶稣基督为上帝之子因而不可能结婚，以及相信玛利亚·抹大拉是妓女的基督徒们，兰登不愿妄加评论。他感到，关于耶稣基督身世的秘密或许很多年来一直是一个谜，但这并未给世界带来什么特别不好的影响。

从这段引文可以看出兰登拒绝将宗教政治化。他相信人们应该拥有信仰的权利，因为这无害于任何人。兰登的这番陈述似乎与他在小说中讲过的其他一些故事相互矛盾。他曾谈到过一些妇女被烧死在火刑柱上以使其他一些妇女在分娩时免于痛苦，而且由于与教会的教义不相符，达·芬奇的画被涂改过。尽管这段引文与兰登的个性不太相符，但作者或许是想以此来反衬提彬的狂热。

KEY FACTS

Full Title

The Da Vinci Code

Author

Dan Brown

Type of Work

Novel

Genre

Thriller

Language

English

Time and Place Written

Early twenty-first century; the United States

Date of First Publication

March 2003

Publisher

Doubleday

Narrator

Third-person, anonymous, omniscient narrator

作品档案

全名

《达·芬奇密码》

作者

丹·布朗

作品类型

小说

流派

惊悚小说

语言

英语

写作时间与地点

21世纪初;美国

初版日期

2003年3月

出版者

双日出版社

叙事者

第三人称,匿名的、全知的叙事者

Point of View

The narrator speaks from the point of view of several characters, describing what they see and hear. The narrator also provides background information and pieces of knowledge unknown to other characters.

Tone

Objective, earnest

Tense

Past

Setting(Time)

The present day

Setting(Place)

Paris, France; Versailles, France; London, England; outskirts of Edinburgh, Scotland

Protagonists

Robert Langdon; Sophie Neveu

Major Conflict

The protagonists attempt to interpret the message left behind by Jacques Saunière and find the hidden secret of the Priory of Sion.

Rising Action

The search for the secret, which is aided by the clues left behind by Jacques Saunière

视角

叙事者从多个人物的视角记述了他们的所见所闻。此外，叙事者还提供了背景知识以及其他人物所不知道的信息。

语气

客观，严肃

时态

过去时

背景(时间)

当代

背景(地点)

法国巴黎；法国凡尔赛；英国伦敦；苏格兰爱丁堡郊外

主人公

罗伯特·兰登；索菲·奈芙

主要冲突

小说中的主人公试图破解雅克·索尼埃留下的信息并找出郇山隐修会隐藏的秘密。

起势情节

在雅克·索尼埃留下的线索的帮助下探寻秘密

Climax

Leigh Teabing reveals himself as the man behind the murders of the Priory of Sion, and Langdon and Sophie discover who killed Jacques Saunière.

Falling Action

The protagonists go to Rosslyn Chapel, where they discover Sophie's family. Langdon goes to the Louvre, where he discovers what he thinks is the resting place of the Grail.

Themes

The false conflict between faith and knowledge; the subjectivity of history; the intelligence of women

Motifs

Ancient and foreign languages; art; sexism

Symbols

Red hair; blood; cell phones

Foreshadowing

Teabing's questions to Sophie about whether she would reveal the secret to the world if she had the choice foreshadows the later revelation of Teabing's obsession with the necessity of revelation. Rémy's slowness in helping Teabing when Silas is assaulting him foreshadows his involvement with Silas and his desire to steal the keystone.

高潮

雷·提彬揭穿他就是杀死郇山隐修会成员的幕后主使，兰登和索菲也发现了是谁杀害了雅克·索尼埃。

收势情节

故事的主人公们来到了罗斯林教堂，他们在那儿找到了索菲的家人。兰登来到卢浮宫，他认为这就是圣杯的安息之所。

主题

信仰与知识的错误之争；历史的主观性；女性的智慧

主题成分

古代语言与外国语言；艺术；男性至上主义

象征

红发；血；手机

预示

提彬曾问索菲，如果她有机会，会不会将秘密公之于众，这为后文展现提彬执迷于揭示秘密的必要性埋下了伏笔。当塞拉斯攻击提彬时，雷米迟迟不肯伸出援手，这预示了他与塞拉斯有关并想偷取楔石。

STUDY QUESTIONS & ESSAY TOPICS

Study Questions

1. What role does wealth play in *The Da Vinci Code*?

The Da Vinci Code, like many international thrillers, operates in a world of extreme privilege. The characters' interactions take place against grand backdrops. Langdon, who is cast as a modest schoolteacher, teaches at Harvard and stays in the Ritz while in Paris to give lectures to assembled cognoscenti. Sophie, a police inspector with a heart of gold, grew up in a big house in Paris—she remembers running from room to room and up and down stairs looking for the clues her grandfather left for her in treasure hunts. Even the revelation of Sophie's grandfather's participation in the ritual of Hieros Gamos takes place in the basement of her grandfather's chateau in Normandy—a rather exalted setting. Saunière is a curator at the Louvre and can bring his granddaughter to see the *Mona Lisa* when there are no pesky tourists to interfere. He is also friends with the head of the Zurich Bank in Paris, André Vernet. Several other highly influential men are also members of the Priory of Sion. In the moral universe of The Da Vinci Code, one can be rich and still be good, but once a certain level of income is exceeded, greed sets in. Sir Leigh Teabing, who has all the money he could possibly want, and whose house is a study in overprivilege, can have anything that his heart desires. He can get across borders without passports and

问题·论题

问·答

1. *在《达·芬奇密码》中财富起到了什么作用?*

和国际上许多惊悚小说一样,《达·芬奇密码》也发生在一个极权的世界。人物的相互作用发生在宏大的背景下。兰登被塑造成一名谦逊的教师,在哈佛执教,在巴黎做讲座时住在丽兹酒店。索菲是有着金子般心灵的警察局破译员,她在巴黎的一所大房子里长大——她记得童年时她曾奔跑于一个又一个的房间,楼上和楼下地寻找祖父为她留下的寻找宝藏的线索。索菲祖父参与神婚仪式的事件也发生在他位于诺曼德的庄园的地下室里,一个十分尊贵的场景中。索尼埃是卢浮宫的馆长,在没有麻烦的游客打扰的时候,他常带着他的孙女看《蒙娜丽莎》。巴黎苏黎世银行行长安德烈韦内特是他的朋友,其他几位有极高影响力的人物也是郇山隐修会的成员。在《达·芬奇密码》这本书的道德世界中,一个人能同时拥有财富和善良,但一旦所得超出了一定范围,贪婪就会随之而来。雷·提彬拥有他想得到的所有钱财,他的房子就是一所超越特权的研究室。他还拥有一切他内心渴望的东西。他能在没有护照的情况下穿越边境,能随时登上飞机。布朗暗示了所有的这些特权造成了提彬道德上的

board planes at the drop of a hat. All of this privilege, Brown implies, ruins Teabing morally and makes it impossible for him to cope mentally with the fact that he can't have the one thing he really wants: knowledge of where the Grail is hidden. Similarly, Aringarosa, the head of Opus Dei, is accustomed to the clout that excessive amounts of money buy for his order. When the Church says that the Pope has decided to disassociate himself from Opus Dei, Aringarosa is shocked, because Opus Dei bailed the Vatican Bank out of trouble a few years earlier. Aringarosa confuses economic power with moral power. This confusion is his moral failing.

Additionally, In Brown's world, people who simply prefer riches, like Bishop Aringarosa, are morally inferior. The difference between crude rich people, like Aringarosa, and rich people with taste, like Teabing, is that the tasteful rich can tell the difference between a good painting and a bad one.

2. How does the novel's drive to educate readers on the history, art history, and symbology behind the mystery relate to its narrative flow?

Part of the thrill of *The Da Vinci Code* is its string of revelations about the historical theories that propel the plot. Many of these revelations come to light during a dramatic action. When, standing in front of Saunière's body, Langdon tells Fache about the significance of the pentacle to pagan worshippers, and makes the differentiation between paganism and devil worship, the fact that he is standing in front of a dead man who has drawn a pentacle on his chest with blood both holds the reader's interest and makes his impromptu lec-

堕落，并且让他不能在精神上面对他极力想得到某件东西却无法拥有的事实：圣杯藏匿地点的消息。同样，阿林加洛沙是天主事公会的头目，他习惯于为执行命令而花大钱所买来的权力。当教会说教皇已经决定要脱离天主事工会时，阿林加洛沙震惊了，因为天主事工会在几年前曾帮助梵蒂冈银行摆脱了麻烦。阿林加洛沙混淆了经济权力和道德力量，这种混乱反映了他道德的沦落。

此外，在布朗的世界里，那些偏爱财富的人和阿林加洛沙主教一样道德低下。粗鲁的有钱人(如阿林加洛沙)与有鉴赏力的有钱人(如提彬)的区别在于有鉴赏力的有钱人能够区分绘画的优劣。

2. *小说对读者进行的谜团背后的历史、艺术史和符号学上的培养导向是如何与其叙事发展相联系的?*

《达·芬奇密码》的部分惊悚之处在于它一连串推动情节的历史理论的披露。其中许多事件是在一个戏剧性的情节中披露出来的。站在索尼埃的尸体前，兰登告诉法希五角星对于异教崇拜者的重要性，并把异教与邪教做了区分。兰登站在一个用血在自己胸口画出一个五角星的死者的前面，这个事实不仅抓住了读者的兴趣，也使他即兴的讲解似乎不太可能——谁会在一具尸体面前解释五角星图案呢？当兰登告诉索

ture seem unlikely—who explains pentacles in front of a corpse? When Langdon tells Sophie about the ancient view of sexual intercourse as a healthy expression of the uniting of man and woman and the power of nature, the reader is interested because Sophie remembers seeing her grandfather participate in that ritual.

When Brown presents information without any dramatic counterpoint, the temptation to skip over paragraphs might set in. For example, Langdon's explanation about Baphomet has little relevance to the plot and might cause impatience. And when the Temple Church is described in detail, it is challenging to follow along, and in the end the clue leading the group there is a red herring.

3. Is *The Da Vinci Code* objective about the mysteries it presents, or is this novel, as many have claimed, written as a diatribe against the Church?

The Da Vinci Code certainly can be interpreted as an offense to the Roman Catholic Church. In the presentation of the themes that have been investigated by historians, such as the missing Gospels, the marriage of Jesus, and the killing of pagans by the Church, the novel examines issues that challenge the historical authority of the Church. Many issues that historians consider controversial are presented as fact. When Langdon and Teabing tell Sophie about the blood lines of Mary Magdalene, they do not tell her that it is merely a theory, not an accepted fact. At the end of the novel, Sophie discovers that she is a descendent of Jesus, a plot twist that suggests that every theory presented in the novel is true.

菲，古代把性行为看作是男女和自然力量结合的一种健康的表达时，读者则又产生了兴趣，因为索菲回忆起她曾看到他的祖父参加了那种仪式。

当布朗没有用戏剧性的对应呈现情节时，读者就会产生想要略过几个段落的欲望。例如，兰登对鲍芙默神的解释与小说情节没什么关联，可能会让读者不耐烦。对于圣殿教堂的细节描绘也很引人入胜，但最终这也变成一条转移视线的干扰线索。

3. *《达·芬奇密码》呈现的一系列秘密是否客观，或者这篇小说是不是像许多人说的那样是对罗马教会的诽谤？*

《达·芬奇密码》的确能被视为对罗马天主教会的抨击。在表现那些已被历史学家研究过的主题时，如遗失的福音、耶稣的婚姻、教会对异教徒的杀害，小说分析了那些挑战教会历史权威的话题。许多历史学家存有争议的话题被作为事实呈现了出来。当兰登和提彬向索菲讲解玛利亚·抹大拉的家族图谱时，他们并没有告诉她那仅仅是一种理论而并非一个获得了认同的事实。在小说结尾，索菲发现她是耶稣的后裔，这一曲折的情节表明出现在小说中的每个理论都是正确的。

But *The Da Vinci Code* doesn't paint a completely negative picture of the Church. By the end of the novel, Brown has revealed that Teabing, who is not associated with the Church, is responsible for the murders of the Priory brothers. This revelation forces the reevaluation of many of the negative implications about the Church that Brown makes at the beginning of the novel: Opus Dei did not order Silas to kill; Bishop Aringarosa feels terrible about the murders of the Brotherhood and offers the victims' families money; the Church itself was planning to separate from Opus Dei and bring its practices more up to date with modern society. And before Silas dies, he feels immense peace thinking of God as a deity of forgiveness, a feeling of reassurance that Bishop Aringarosa has given him. Silas turns into an example of a person who has been rescued by his faith.

但《达·芬奇密码》并没有把教会描画得完全消极。在小说结尾，布朗揭示是与教会无关的提彬密谋杀害了郇山隐修会的成员。由于布朗曾在小说的开始部分对教会做出过消极的推断，所以这一事件的披露促使人们对此要进行重新评判：天主事工会并没有指使塞拉斯去杀人；阿林加洛沙主教对修士会成员遭到谋杀的事感到难过，并为受害者的家属提供抚恤金；罗马教会打算与天主事工会脱离关系，并使它的教规更符合现代社会。在塞拉斯临死之前，他想到上帝是宽厚之神，于是感到了极大安宁，并感到了阿林加洛沙对他的信任。塞拉斯成为了一个人因为信仰而获救的范例。

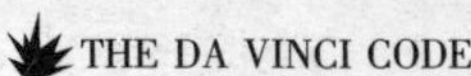

Suggested Essay Topics

1. Does *The Da Vinci Code* opens doors to discussion about religion, as Dan Brown has said, or does it close them?

2. Is the depiction of women in this novel a tribute to their intelligence, or does it subtly uphold the patriarchal structures it purports to rail against?

3. In what ways is *The Da Vinci Code* similar to other popular novels in the thriller genre? In what ways does it depart from them?

4. How does *The Da Vinci Code* juxtapose ancient and modern worlds?

5. How do Langdon's flashbacks to his teaching work in the States contribute to the narrative?

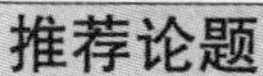

推荐论题

1.《达·芬奇密码》是为有关宗教的讨论开启了大门，还是像丹·布朗说的，关闭了大门？

2. 小说中对女性的描绘是对她们智慧的赞扬，还是巧妙地赞成了它所反对的家长制制度？

3.《达·芬奇密码》与其他流行的惊悚小说有哪些相似之处？ 又有哪些不同？

4.《达·芬奇密码》怎样并置了古代和现代两个世界？

5. 兰登对他在美国执教工作的倒叙是如何为小说叙述服务的？

REVIEW & RESOURCES

回味·深入

Quiz 四选一

1. What striking physical feature does Silas possess?

(A) He is an albino

(B) He has only nine fingers

(C) He has horrible eczema

(D) One of his ears is missing

2. Who is the artist whose painting Saunière pulls from the wall of the Louvre in order to trigger the alarm?

(A) Fragonard

(B) Poussin

(C) Caravaggio

(D) Da Vinci

3. At which university does Robert Langdon teach?

(A) Oxford

(B) Harvard

(C) Yale

(D) Princeton

4. Where does Silas wear his punishment belt?

(A) His back

(B) His arm

(C) His face

（D） His thigh

5. What architect created the entrance to the Louvre?

（A） Frank Gehry

（B） I.M. Pei

（C） Howard Roark

（D） Frank Lloyd Wright

6. What animal does Collet compare Fache to?

（A） A bull

（B） A snake

（C） A fish

（D） A ferret

7. What does Jacques Saunière draw on himself before dying?

（A） A circle

（B） A smiley face

（C） A pentacle

（D） A maze

8. What color is the namesake of the famous sundial line in Saint-Suplice?

（A） Rose

（B） Violet

（C） Purple

（D） Fuchsia

9. What flower is depicted on Saunière's key?

（A） Lily

(B) Rose
(C) Fleur-de-lis
(D) Lilac

10. What kind of birds normally frequent St. James' Park in London, where the Teacher and Rémy meet?

(A) Seagulls
(B) Pelicans
(C) Doves
(D) Swans

11. Which book of the Bible contains the verse that the priory has written on the keystone?

(A) Deuteronomy
(B) Luke
(C) Exodus
(D) Job

12. What weapon does Silas use to kill Sister Sandrine?

(A) A pistol
(B) A slingshot
(C) A candle stand
(D) A sword

13. What is Rémy allergic to?

(A) Wheat
(B) Peanuts
(C) Pollen
(D) Dogs

14. What kind of wristwatch does Robert Langdon wear?

（A） Mickey Mouse

（B） Rolex

（C） Timex

（D） Burger King giveaway

15. What rank does Leigh Teabing hold?

（A） Lord

（B） Captain

（C） Knight

（D） General

16. Which Da Vinci painting features a representation of Mary Magdalene?

（A） Madonna of the Rocks

（B） The Vitruvian Man

（C） Mona Lisa

（D） The Last Supper

17. What famous scientist's tomb is the site of the last clue?

（A） Sir Isaac Newton

（B） Tycho Kepler

（C） Galileo Galilei

（D） Marie Curie

18. Where is the bug hidden in Saunière's office?

（A） The stapler

（B） The hand lotion dispenser

（C） The knight replica on his desk

(D) The doormat

19. What color is the Magdalene's hair?

(A) Platinum blonde
(B) Red
(C) Chestnut brown
(D) Manic Panic blue

20. What does the altar boy in the Temple Church do when Silas grabs him?

(A) Wets his pants
(B) Kicks Silas in the groin
(C) Runs away
(D) Screams

21. What piece of furniture does Langdon put the box underneath in Teabing's study?

(A) The footstool
(B) The dog
(C) The telephone
(D) The divan

22. What is the notable poetic structure of the poem inside the cryptex box?

(A) Iambic pentameter
(B) Blank verse
(C) Sonnet
(D) Sestina

23. What disease disabled Leigh Teabing?

(A) Gout

(B) Multiple sclerosis

(C) Polio

(D) Cerebral palsy

24. What does Rémy drink when he is about to untie Silas?

(A) Red Stripe

(B) Vodka

(C) A martini

(D) Cherry Coke

25. What kind of car do Rémy, Teabing, Langdon and Sophie use to escape from the chateau?

(A) A Range Rover

(B) A Jaguar

(C) A Porsche

(D) A smart car

Answer Key:

1.A 2.C 3.B 4.D 5.B 6.A 7.C 8.A 9.C

10.B 11.D 12.C 13.B 14.A 15.C 16.D 17.A

18.C 19.B 20.A 21.D 22.A 23.C 24.B 25.A

Suggestions for Further Reading

相关链接

BAIGENT, MICHAEL, et al. *Holy Blood, Holy Grail*. New York: Dell, 1983.

BRADLEY, MARION ZIMMER. *The Mists of Avalon*. New York: Del Ray, 1987.

KELLMEYER, STEVE. *Fact and Fiction in* The Da Vinci Code. Peoria, Illinois: Bridegroom Press, 2004.

LELOUP, JEAN-YVES, et al. *The Gospel of Mary Magdalene*. Rochester, Vermont: Inner Traditions, 2002.

PAGELS, ELAINE. *The Gnostic Gospels*. New York: Vintage, 1989.

PICKNETT, LYNN and CLIVE PRINCE. *The Templar Revelation: Secret Guardians of the True Identity of Christ*. Carmichael, California: Touchstone Books, 1998.

STARBIRD, MARGARET. *The Goddess in the Gospels: Reclaiming the Sacred Feminine*. Rochester, Vermont: Bear & Co., 1998.

———. *The Woman with the Alabaster Jar: Mary Magdalene and the Holy Grail*. Rochester, Vermont: Bear & Co., 1993.

WELBORN, AMY. *Decoding Da Vinci: The Facts behind the Fiction of* The Da Vinci Code. Huntington, Indiana: Our Sunday Visitor, 2004.

哈佛蓝星双语名著导读(共98册)

Today's Most Popular Study Guides

悲剧·喜剧系列

双城记(A Tale of Two Cities)
炼狱(The Crucible)
人与鼠(Of Mice and Men)
老人与海(The Old Man and the Sea)
推销员之死(Death of the Salesman)
最蓝的眼睛(The Bluest Eye)
一个人的和平(A Separate Peace)
瓦解(Things Fall Apart)
苔丝(Tess of the D'Urbervilles)
欲望号街车(A Street Car Named Desire)
卡斯特桥市长(The Mayor of Casterbridge)
安娜·卡列尼娜(Anna Karenina)
基督山伯爵(The Count of Monte Cristo)

浪漫·传奇系列

小妇人(Little Women)
尤利西斯(Ulysses)
堂吉诃德(Don Quixote)
汤姆·索亚历险记(The Adventures of Tom Sawyer)
黑暗的中心(Heart of Darkness)
鲁宾逊漂流记(Robinson Crusoe)
红字(The Scarlet Letter)
金银岛(Treasure Island)
哈克贝里·芬历险记(The Adventures of Huckelberry Finn)
白鲸(Moby Dick)
坎特伯雷故事集(The Canterbury Tales)

野性的呼唤(The Call of the Wild)
英国病人(The English Patient)
呼啸山庄(Wuthering Heights)
简·爱(Jane Eyre)
爱玛(Emma)
傲慢与偏见(Pride and Prejudice)

史诗·战争系列

所罗门之歌(Song of Solomon)
失乐园(Paradise Lost)
悲惨世界(Les Miserables)
战争与和平(War and Peace)
广岛(Hiroshima)
永别了,武器(A Farewell to Arms)
愤怒的葡萄(The Grapes of Wrath)
西线无战事(All Quiet on the Western Front)
丧钟为谁而鸣(For Whom the Bell Tolls)
第二十二条军规(Catch-22)
红色英勇勋章(The Red Badge of Courage)
太阳依旧升起(The Sun Also Rises)

寓言·幻想系列

一个青年艺术家的画像(A Portrait of the Artist as a Young Man)
局外人(The Stranger)
瓦尔登湖(Walden)
格列佛游记(Gulliver's Travels)
华氏451度(Fahrenheit 451)
弗兰肯斯坦(Frankenstein)
珍珠(The Pearl)
蝇王(Lord of the Flies)

隐形人(Invisible Man)
美丽新世界(Brave New World)
浮士德博士(Doctor Faustus)
爱丽丝漫游奇境记与镜中世界
(Alice's Adventures in Wonderland and through the Looking-Glass)
苏菲的世界(Sophie's World)
麦田守望者(The Catcher in the Rye)
相约星期二(Tuesdays with Morrie)

现代·现实系列

了不起的盖茨比(The Great Gatsby)
他们的眼睛望着上帝(Their Eyes Were Watching God)
安琪拉的灰烬(Angela's Ashes)
觉醒(The Awakening)
宠儿(Beloved)
土生子(Native Son)
罪与罚(Crime and Punishment)
喧哗与骚动(Sound and Fury)
喜福会(The Joy Luck Club)
远大前程(Great Expectation)
汤姆叔叔的小屋(Uncle Tom's Cabin)
雾都孤儿(Oliver Twist)
屠场(The Jungle)
玩偶之家(A Doll's House)
黑孩子(Black Boy)
印度之行(A Passage to India)
都柏林人(The Dubliners)
包法利夫人(Madam Bovary)
艰难时世(Hard Times)

美国梦(American Dream)

生命中不能承受之轻(The Unbearable Lightness of Being)

魔幻·悬念系列

魔戒(The Lord of Rings)

魔戒前传:霍比特人(The Hobbit)

哈利·波特与魔法石(Harry Potter and the Socerer's Stone)

哈里·波特与密室(Harry Potter and the Chamber of Secrets)

哈里·波特与阿兹卡班的囚徒(Harry Potter and the Prisoner of Azkaban)

哈里·波特与火焰杯(Harry Potter and the Goblet of Fire)

哈里·波特与凤凰社(Harry Potter and The Order of the Phoenix)

哈里·波特与混血王子(Harry Potter and the Half-Blood Prince)

哈里·波特与死亡圣器(Harry Potter and the Deathly Hallows)

百年孤独(One Hundred Years of Solitude)

达·芬奇密码(The Da Vinci Code)

月亮宝石(The Moonstone)

东方快车谋杀案(Murder on the Orient Express)

纳尼亚传奇:狮子·女巫·魔衣橱(The Lion, the Witch and the Wardrobe)

好莱坞经典名剧系列

钢琴课(The Piano Lesson)

冷山(Cold Mountain)

飘(Gone with the Wind)

热铁皮屋顶上的猫(Cat on a Hot Tin Roof)

杀死一只知更鸟(To kill a Mocking Bird)

查理与巧克力工厂(Charlie and the Chocolate Factory)